Storyline 2.0

FINDING YOUR SUBPLOT IN GOD'S STORY

By **Donald Miller**

INDEX

Storyline is a personal development process thousands have used to plan their lives.

Storyline is based on the formula screenwriters and novelists use to create stories. The eight modules that comprise Storyline will help you live a better story and as such experience a meaningful life. Once you've completed Storyline you'll have clarity about what you're doing and the courage to face life's challenges. Storyline will also provide a decision filter you can use for all important decisions.

As a framework, Storyline can be laid over a therapeutic process developed by Dr. Viktor Frankl called Logotherapy. Logos is a Greek word for meaning or spirit and therapy means healing. Storyline, then, offers healing by helping people find a sense of meaning in their lives.

Thank you for wanting to live a better story. We believe your story was a blank page given to you by God and to write a great story on that page is a noble pursuit and a gift to the world.

A note to Storyline clients;

I have a friend who is a lawyer who always gives clients the same counsel. He asks to them to sit palms up.

No kidding. When his clients are being deposed or questioned, he asks them to sit with their hands on their knees, palms to the sky, answering each question honestly and without reactionary defense.

The concept is genius. When we sit palms up, we are less likely to be cynical, less likely to lash out and less likely to reject the truths that are good for us.

As you go through Storyline, there may be ideas you disagree with. I only ask that you remain palms up.

This process is a therapeutic process derived from a theory developed by man. While it is based on sacred truths, it isn't perfect. And yet to reject it on a single disagreement could derail you from an experience that might prove healing.

As you create your Storyline, maintain an attitude of being palms up. Accept that which helps you and softly reject what isn't helpful.

In the end, while not being perfect, we believe you'll find the process healing.

INTRODUCTION

A wise man once taught me a mental trick. He said if you want to live a meaningful life, imagine yourself ten years from now, then ask yourself what you'll wish you'd done by then. Then do those things.

It's a good trick, if you think about it. I've used it many times. It's amazing how priorities float to the top when we consider our lives in hindsight.

In fact, the most humbling perspective I've had came from taking this trick to its furthest point-- to the end of my life. I sat and wondered what would have been important if I were able to attend my own funeral.

Of course, relationships became a priority. I wanted to have been more forgiving and more loving. I wanted to have spent more time with people and have told them how much I cared about them. And suddenly my career didn't seem as important. I no longer worried whether I made a lot of money or was famous. In fact, I saw the effort I spent "getting ahead" as a waste of time.

But what mattered, more than anything, was that I had been used by God for some small purpose.

It was an amazing epiphany and I'm grateful.

So from the desire to be used by God came some obvious questions: What in the world is God doing? I mean that quite literally: What is God doing in the world? What is He working on? And where can I plug in? Does God give specific assignments or do we get to decide for ourselves? And how do we hear from God?

OUR STORY IS A SUBPLOT IN GOD'S STORY

As a writer, I see the Bible as a story. It's a story about unrequited love. It's a story about a God who loves a world that, for the most part, ignores Him. It's a sad story, but it has a great ending. In the end, God gets the girl back.

In a way, that story has already been written. I mean it hasn't happened yet, but for a God who lives outside time, it's as good as done. And yet, the role you and I get to play in that story is still unfolding. And not only this, but we actually get to decide our little part.

All epic stories have subplots, and each of our lives is a subplot. What we want to accomplish at Storyline is simple: We want to help people live a great subplot in God's story.

You've likely heard of a life plan. I once met with a guy for two days to create my life plan. And it was worth it. I learned an enormous amount about myself and had a great deal more clarity in life. That particular life plan was more about my career, though, than my overall life. Storyline is about your career, for sure, but it's also about the rest of life. It's about creating a great overall human experience.

Storyline has one goal in mind, which is that when you get to the end of your life and the credits roll, you'll have lived a completely meaningful life. And we think this is possible only when you understand your life is a subplot in a greater epic.

Before a writer sits down to write a novel or screenplay, they often chart out the story, scene by scene. Storyline follows the same process, only you won't be plotting out a fictional story, you'll be plotting out your life.

Our hope at Storyline is this process will be eye opening for you. By the end, we believe you'll be able to see more clearly what God is doing, and we hope you'll find a subplot you were designed to live.

What is God doing in the world? We will find out. And *what part does He want you to play?* We'll tackle that question too.

We are grateful you've decided to enter into God's story and map out your subplot within that story. We think when you look back on life, you'll be glad you did.

Sincerely,

Donald Miller
Portland, Oregon

STORYLINE STARTS WITH GOD

Of course, the story of the world is not about us. When people plan their stories around themselves, they come to the end and realize their stories were empty. They realize they weren't the sun and when they forced the world to revolve around themselves, they had no capacity to bring life to those they loved.

When we plan our lives around God, though, we find ourselves in a grand adventure. Our lives are no longer our own, they belong to Him. An individual's story makes more sense as part of a larger epic. The cosmos is too big a stage and our time too short to think it's about us.

When we live our lives as though we are the star of the show, nobody likes our story. Nobody learns from it or is inspired by it or thinks it's beautiful.

At Storyline, we are convinced we were designed to submit to somebody larger than ourselves, somebody who knows all and sees all, somebody we can trust. We believe that somebody is God.

I doubt all those who go through Storyline believe in God, but we encourage you, perhaps in the tradition of Alcoholics Anonymous, to simply understand it makes no sense to believe the universe is all about you.

As you go through Storyline, simply pray and ask God to be involved. Even if you've never been a person of faith, don't worry about it. Just pray and talk to God and submit your story to Him. We believe He will meet you as you partner with Him to live a meaningful life.

HOW DOES STORYLINE WORK?

As we've said a few times now, Storyline takes you through a process similar to what screenwriters and novelists use to write a great story.

Great stories have one thing in common: they are clear. As such, Storyline is all about gaining mental clarity. If a character doesn't know what they want, the story gets muddled. The same is true in life. And if the conflict isn't clearly identified, the story drags, as it does in life.

As you go through the process transfer what you discover about yourself to our online Dashboard. The service is free and by transferring your responses (even if you never return to the Dashboard) you'll have much greater retention of what you learn.

To start a free Storyline Dashboard, simply go to **MySubplot.com** and register. Once you're done with the process, you can bookmark your individual page and use it to edit your story for years to come.

HOW TO USE STORYLINE

AS A PERSONAL GUIDE: If you use Storyline to create your personal life plan, the process should take you several days. Storyline is a reflective guide, so make sure to take all the time you need.

Remember, Storyline is based on psychologist Viktor Frankl's Logotherapy and as such takes time and reflection. You won't figure out your life right away, but you'll have all the tools and knowledge to gain clarity and start making better decisions.

IN A SMALL GROUP: If you're leading a group through Storyline, simply break the modules into weeks. We recommend meeting eight times, the first as an introduction in which you hand out books, get to know each other and discuss the introductory material; then tackle one or two modules each week.

While the small group time is a great place to share your story, the time of reflection will still be personal and each member of the small group will need to set aside hours during the week to complete the modules.

IN THERAPY: If you are going through Storyline with a life coach, spiritual director or counselor, simply follow their lead. They will know best how to help you clarify your ambitions, engage rather than avoid conflict and find redemptive perspectives toward your negative turns.

TIPS ON GETTING THE MOST OUT OF STORYLINE

PRAY: We believe God has you on the planet for a reason. We also believe God wants to interact with you in living a better story. When you pray, invite God into your story and create your Storyline with Him.

EDIT AS YOU GO: Great writers know stories are always in process and nothing is fixed. So feel free to create your Storyline and then edit it for the rest of your life. The only things that are static in life are dead. Your story should be alive and ever evolving.

TAKE YOUR TIME: Some of the modules can be completed in a few minutes but others may take hours or days. Remember, the process will give back what you invest and more, so be patient and persistent.

COMPLETE THE PROCESS: Any screenwriter who gets lazy ends up making a terrible movie. Writing is hard work and it takes discipline. Agree with yourself that you'll finish this project and understand you will face resistance. Showing up to do this work is a revolutionary act. Face the resistance and you'll be rewarded.

HILIGHT THIS BOOK: The online Dashboard is great, but without the modules you won't get much out of Storyline. Storyline is about reflection and intention. As you go through this book, mark it up. Hilight what you find interesting and write down your thoughts. We printed this book on heavier paper so you could take plenty of great notes without damaging the pages.

USE MYSUBPLOT.COM: We've designed **MySubplot.com** as a tool to help lock in what you've learned. Each time you enter a story you'll be recording goals and further thinking through the stories you want to tell. Use this tool for as many stories as you like, then share the stories you are attempting to live with friends.

ACCESS YOUR HEART: While Storyline will make you more productive and efficient, this isn't about turning you into a cog in a machine. Storyline is about acknowledging God created you as a whole human being with a mind and heart, with fears and desires. Storyline is about living a meaningful life, so as you move forward, consider more than your career. Consider your relationships and your dreams. Living a great story is about learning what it means to be human and fully alive. Great stories often start with people who have found their hearts.

WHAT IS THE STORY OF GOD?

A long time ago while writing a screenplay I learned the basic formula for telling a story. A story is simply this: a character that wants something and overcomes conflict to get it.

Think about it. What's your favorite movie? Isn't it about a character (or characters) that wants something and overcomes conflict to get it?

Almost every story is.

So when we ask *what is the story of God,* we are really asking *What does God want,* and *what does God have to overcome to get it?*

WHAT DOES GOD WANT?

While we can know a lot about God from the pages of Scripture, He's mostly a mystery. We really don't know much about what God's been up to for all eternity, and we only know a little about what will happen after we die. The prophet Isaiah says:

"For my thoughts are not your thoughts, neither are your ways my ways," declares the Lord. (Isaiah 55:8)

That said, we know some important characteristics and attributes about God. We know, for example, He is good and loving. We know He is just and attentive. We know He hears us and is mindful of us.

One of God's most obvious characteristics is that He wants to connect. While God doesn't force Himself on people, He does respond to those who want to know Him (but does not respond to those who test Him.)

God likes others and does not live in isolation. In fact, He is so intimate with Jesus and the Holy Spirit they are described as one. And together, the Trinity created angels and other creatures so they could enjoy Him and He could enjoy them.

Because God is so good, He created us to interact with Him as well. Given His loving nature, the most generous thing God could do was to create other beings to enjoy Him. So that's why you exist.

You exist to enjoy a relationship with God.

I remember driving in the middle of the night through the high desert years ago with a friend who teaches the Bible at a local college. We were miles from any city hoping to make Mt. Bachelor for sunrise when my friend pulled his truck over and got out. He began walking down the road, away from the truck and into the darkness. I watched as he laid down on the asphalt, staring into the heavens.

I got out of the truck and asked what in the world he was doing. *Looking at the stars,* he said, *Join me.*

I joined my friend and remembered for the first time in years how vast the heavens were. Because we were at such a high elevation and so far from the light pollution of the city, the stars may have been thicker than I'd ever seen.

I asked my friend why he thought God did all this, made all these stars that seem to be so superfluous.

My friend said, *it's obvious why He did it, Don. He made the stars to dazzle you.*

What does God want? *He wants you. He wants to interact with you, enjoy time with you, have a relationship with you and enjoy the fact that you, in turn, enjoy Him.*

WHAT DOES GOD HAVE TO OVERCOME TO GET WHAT HE WANTS?

Have you ever noticed that God doesn't seem to be around? I mean it's obvious the world is a special place and it's sometimes hard to believe all of it could be an accident, but it would be great if God would show up and claim His work. But He doesn't.

The reality is God is separated from us in a spiritual sense. We are not intimate with God the way we were designed to be. But why did God let this happen and what is He doing about it?

Have you ever met somebody with a controlling personality? A controlling person doesn't like the fact other people have a will. A controlling person knows what's right and wrong (or at least thinks they do) and gets angry when people don't obey. Controlling people get what they want by being manipulative.

Controlling people, though, have a hard time feeling loved. Even though they can scare people into staying with them, deep down they know the love isn't authentic. To have real love, you have to allow people to walk away. If they stay then the love is sincere and if they go, it's a sad loss but the truth is the person just didn't love them back.

Love is all about risk and it's not for the faint of heart. A controlling person is driven by fear, not strength. People are controlling because they fear the risk inherently involved in relationships. The more fearless a person is, the less controlling he becomes.

Now, here's a truth that may surprise you: God isn't afraid and so God isn't controlling. He actually gives people the opportunity to walk away. This is the only way God can have a sincere, authentic and loving relationship with His creation.

And that's why the world is such a troubling place.

Because God is not a controlling dictator, He gave mankind a way to walk away. Tragically, this happened at the Fall of Man. When the first of God's creation fell away, God had no choice but to separate Himself. It's not that He stopped loving us, it's just that we walked away from who He was, a perfect and loving being.

Now remember, God wants to connect. And even though mankind walked away, God still loves us. So what does a perfectly loving being do when the object of His desire walks away?

He goes after them.

The reason God sent His Son to die on a cross wasn't to technically fulfill some kind of law. Though the law was fulfilled in Christ, the motive behind that selfless act was love. God sent His son because He loves us and misses us.

And yet we still have a will. Christ's death on the cross was the ultimate act of love, the largest bouquet of flowers in history, the sentiment of a million love songs played out in real life. But because He is not controlling, we are still given the freedom to respond any way we choose.

So what does God have to overcome to get what He wants? *He has to overcome the distracted and doubtful nature of those He loves. He has to invite them to love Him back and participate with Him in His will.*

HOW IS GOD OVERCOMING CONFLICT?

All the major characters in Scripture are participating with God to save many lives. God isn't just trying to get people to heaven, He's also creating order and justice, providing food and water and systems that will generate beautiful communities.

God does not force Himself on others, but He does invite us to participate in His effort to save many lives. The way God is overcoming the conflict in the world is through us, through our words and hands and feet. If we are willing, we get to participate in what God is doing in the world.

A TIMELINE OF GOD'S STORY

God has been alive for all of eternity, so His story is vast. We can't know all of it. In fact, it's safe to say we know very little. However, Scripture gives us a peek and that peek helps us understand where we fit into God's story.

Screenwriters and novelists will often create a visual timeline of their stories to help get their heads around the journey of their characters.

Stories are made up of positive and negative turns. When we put these positive and negative turns in chronological order and then place them on a graph, we make what amounts to an emotional map that helps us understand what a character has gone through.

Later in the Storyline process, we'll be making a timeline of your life so far. For now, though, here's a timeline of what we know about God's life (See page 16).

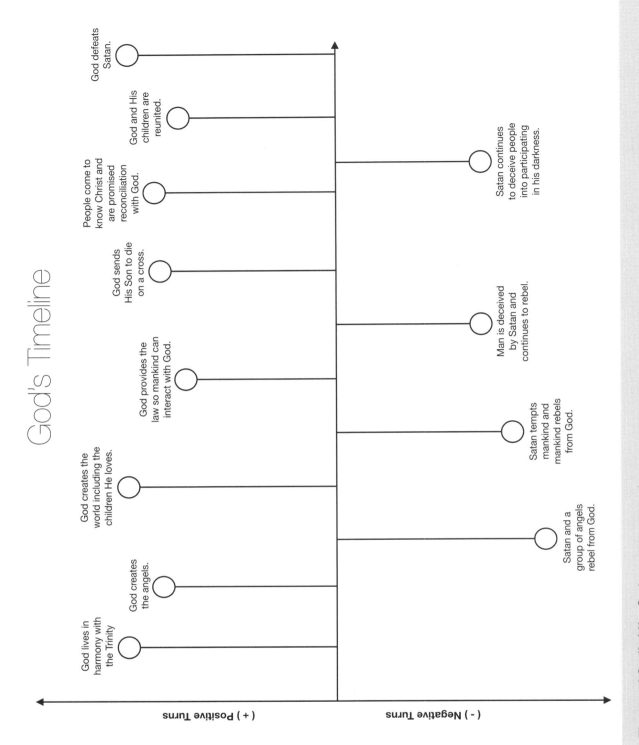

God's Timeline

Positive Turns (+)

- God lives in harmony with the Trinity
- God creates the angels.
- God creates the world including the children He loves.
- God provides the law so mankind can interact with God.
- God sends His Son to die on a cross.
- People come to know Christ and are promised reconciliation with God.
- God and His children are reunited.
- God defeats Satan.

Negative Turns (-)

- Satan and a group of angels rebel from God.
- Satan tempts mankind and mankind rebels from God.
- Man is deceived by Satan and continues to rebel.
- Satan continues to deceive people into participating in his darkness.

Theme of God's Life: God wants to connect.

From this timeline, we can see not only what God has been through, but where we are in His story. We are in the part of the story where Satan continues to deceive people into participating in his darkness.

But, of course, it doesn't have to be this way. We can be sober in our thinking and participate in God's effort to love the world. God has a part for you and me in this story.

Thought for reflection: *Consider marking your place in God's story. Take a pen and simply circle the place where you are today on the timeline. It's a simple exercise, but you'll want to remember where you are in God's story when you create your own subplot.*

1

A Character
that wants something
and overcomes conflict
to get it.

"For you created my inmost being, you knit me together in my mother's womb."
- Psalm 139:13

"I'm drawn particularly to stories that evolve out of the character of the protagonist."
- David McCullough, Author of *John Adams*, *1776* and *Truman*

SECTION ONE
What is Your Story?

THE STORY HAS CHANGED

Have you ever wondered where you fit in the overall epic of humanity?

I mean if you could look at a narrative map of eternal history, where would your story be placed on that map?

Well, here's where you are:

Let's say I invited you to the house for a barbecue. The intent would be to enjoy each other's company, mingle with friends, eat some great food and maybe play some games. But let's say when you got there something terrible had happened. Let's say the propane tank for the grill exploded and a lot of people were injured.

Essentially, that's where we are in the history of the world. Things are not as they were intended to be and we're showing up on the scene after the accident.

Christian theology states something terrible happened in world history. We refer to this event as the Fall of Man. Specifics are vague, but we do know mankind walked away from God and the results were devastating. I suspect we will learn more once we are with God, but for now, the reality that our story has been corrupted is rather obvious.

There's no question the intention of God's story has changed. He intended to create a time and place and creation to interact with Him, but because mankind chose their own way, He's distant. And He's not distant because He wants to be, He's distant because He has to be. His nature cannot mix and mingle with those who don't want anything to do with Him. Let's just say He has a great sense of boundaries.

He's not panicking about it, because He already knows how the story ends. But He's calling on us to help.

I've heard the definition of sanity as the ability to align ourselves to reality. If that's the case, denying something terrible has happened is the epitome of insanity. After all, the subject of the nightly news is always the same: What's wrong with the world and how can we fix it?

But none of our earthly governments are going to fix our problem. The problem is we were designed to be in relationship with God and until we are reunited with Him, things aren't going to work right.

SO WHAT DO WE DO?

If you showed up at a barbecue and there had been a terrible accident, the sober and sane thing to do would be to put down the potato salad and address those who were hurting.

Of course, life is not so simple as a barbecue. It's complicated. There are all kinds of ways people have been hurt. Marriages are in trouble, people suffer from self hatred and temptations to numb ourselves from the pain are everywhere.

To be sure, there is nothing we can do to restore life to where it was before the Fall. Christian leaders who say you can be the person God designed you to be are well intentioned, but being the person God designed you to be is not possible in this life.

WE WILL NOT BE PERFECT IN THIS LIFETIME

The only descriptor we have of man before the fall is their identity was so wrapped up in God they could walk around naked and not know it (Genesis 2-3). Can you imagine? I am so insecure I always know when I'm naked. I never go to the store and realize I forgot my wallet and, well, my clothes.

When we are reunited with God, all our insecurities will be gone. We will be so enthralled by His company we will lose ourselves in comparison. This is what it was like to walk with God before the fall. We were so enamored with Him, we were hardly aware of ourselves.

So the next time you read a book that says you can be the person God designed you to be, flip over to the back cover and look at the author's picture. If the author is wearing clothes, get your money back.

We will be the person God designed us to be when we are reunited with Him and until then we have to wait in patience, hope and faith. There will be no perfecting of ourselves this side of God's return so we might as well stop kicking ourselves around about our faults.

GOD IS INVITING US TO PARTICIPATE WITH HIM IN SAVING MANY LIVES

The story of Joseph takes up more space in the book of Genesis than any other story. The creation of the earth and the fall of man are summarized in only a few chapters, while the story of Joseph is given 13.

And it's no wonder. It's a remarkable story with many ups and downs and it has a great deal to teach us about how God interacts with humanity.

To be sure, Joseph has to go through a lot of hard times. But God is always with him.

At the end of the story Joseph says something interesting. He says all the hard events in his life were given him so God could use him to save many lives. (Genesis 50:19)

In fact, there are two other places in the story where Joseph makes it known the point of his subplot was to save many lives. While Joseph may have had no idea why the things that were happening to him were really happening, he figured it out by the end. He was participating in God's effort to save many lives.

The life-theme of every major character in Scripture, every leader who follows God is the same: They are participating with God to save many lives.

Even poor old Jonah is used by God to save many lives. God never turns Jonah into a puppet on a string, but he makes it hard to say no. God is going to use Jonah to save the people of Nineveh whether Jonah likes it or not.

Abraham is used by God to save many lives and so is Moses. David saves lives (when he cooperates with God) and so does Solomon with all his wisdom.

The Apostles who built the early church were single focused: save many lives!

If we would like to participate in what God is doing in the world, we must help Him save many lives.

WHAT DOES PARTICIPATING WITH GOD TO SAVE MANY LIVES LOOK LIKE?

When we look at the life of a person who is participating with God to save many lives, it's a roller coaster.

We'd think when God decides to change the world through us it would feel as though we'd won the lottery. But it's never that way in scripture. When God works through a person, their life is often hard.

Joseph's Timeline

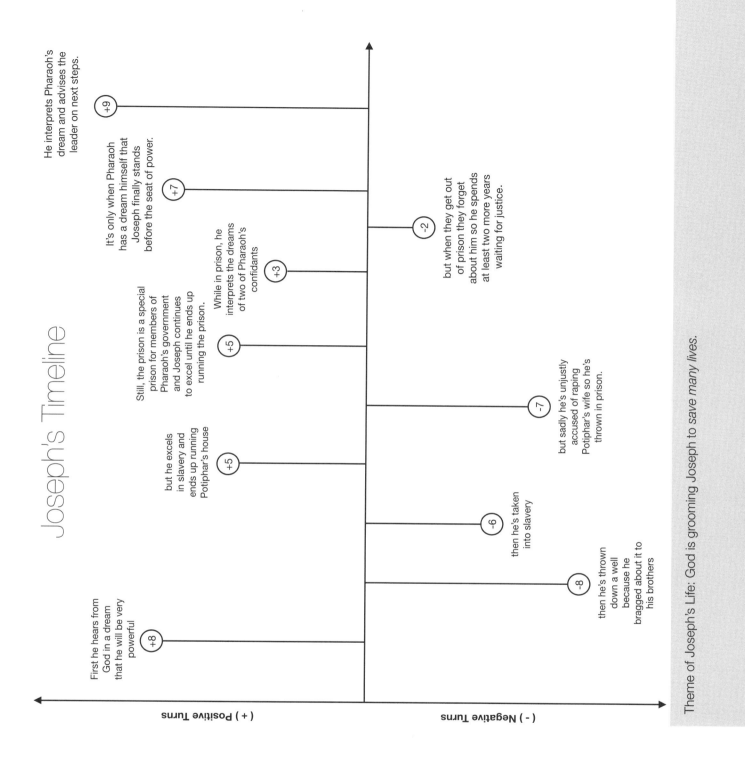

(+) Positive Turns

(−) Negative Turns

First he hears from God in a dream that he will be very powerful +8

but he excels in slavery and ends up running Potiphar's house +5

Still, the prison is a special prison for members of Pharaoh's government and Joseph continues to excel until he ends up running the prison. +5

While in prison, he interprets the dreams of two of Pharaoh's confidants +3

It's only when Pharaoh has a dream himself that Joseph finally stands before the seat of power. +7

He interprets Pharaoh's dream and advises the leader on next steps. +9

then he's thrown down a well because he bragged about it to his brothers −8

then he's taken into slavery −6

but sadly he's unjustly accused of raping Potiphar's wife so he's thrown in prison. −7

but when they get out of prison they forget about him so he spends at least two more years waiting for justice. −2

Theme of Joseph's Life: God is grooming Joseph to *save many lives.*

Let's go back to the life of Joseph and use his life as an example. (Genesis 37-50)

As I've said, screenwriters and novelists use the terms *positive turn* and *negative turn* when they talk about the events their characters go through. We will use the same terminology to better understand how God has ordered our lives.

As we read the story of Joseph (a man called by God and watched over by God from beginning to end) let's consider how many positive and negative turns he experienced.

First he hears from God in a dream that he will be very powerful (positive turn +8), then he's thrown down a well because he bragged about it to his brothers (negative turn -8), then he's taken into slavery (-6), but he excels in slavery and ends up running Potiphar's house (+5) (Potiphar was a commander in Pharaoh's military), but sadly he's unjustly accused of raping Potiphar's wife so he's thrown in prison. (-7) Still, the prison is a special prison for members of Pharaoh's government and Joseph continues to excel until he ends up running the prison. (+5) While in prison, he interprets the dreams of two of Pharaoh's confidants,(+3) but when they get out of prison they forget about him so he spends at least two more years waiting for justice.(-2) It's only when Pharaoh has a dream himself that Joseph finally stands before the seat of power. (+7)

Because of all of Joseph's negative turns, though, he is uniquely capable to advise Pharaoh. He interprets Pharaoh's dream and advises the leader on next steps. Pharoah then makes Joseph second in command. (+9)

And why was Joseph qualified? For many reasons. First, he could empathize with the marginalized (thrown in a well), then he understood how the military worked and he'd need a military to expand government powers (he learned about the military by running Potiphar's house) and because he ran the prison, he had intimate knowledge of every facet of Pharaoh's government.

Because of the positive and negative turns in Joseph's life, he was uniquely qualified for the power he'd been promised. And not only this, but by the time he'd been given power, his heart had changed from an arrogant young kid to a wise and powerful leader. (Genesis 37-50)

WHAT IF THE POSITIVE AND NEGATIVE TURNS OF YOUR LIFE HAVE PREPARED YOU FOR SOMETHING GREAT?

What if the events of your life have prepared you for something too?

I'll never forget the first time I created my timeline. I was working with a life-coach in Colorado and he asked about the positive and negative turns of my life. I sat on his couch and reflected back, thinking about my father leaving, and shortly thereafter a youth pastor stepping in and acting as a father figure. I thought about my first heartbreak and then the successes in my writing career. In all, there was a lot of joy and a lot of pain.

My life coach then transferred my positive and negative turns to a timeline, a large piece of butcher paper he'd taped to the wall. When he was done, he sat back and asked if I could see a theme.

Indeed, I was amazed. It was clear to me. The theme of my life was: God was with me. All those times I felt alone, God was there. When my father left, God was raising up a father figure. And when I made mistakes, God helped me learn. Every time I turned to God with a problem, He was there to help.

It often didn't feel that way in the moment, but looking back, it was obvious.

My life coach then asked me to write down the theme of my life. I wrote down "God is always with me."

Since then, I've edited the theme of my life to read: *To share the story of God and help others find their subplots in His story.*

Today, I use that theme as a decision filter. In other words, I reject almost any opportunity that does not reflect the theme of my life.

I do this because of my training as a writer. I know firsthand writers must make tough decisions. A good writer will throw away any brilliant scene that is not in keeping with the theme of his story. And a person who knows their Storyline will do the same.

The best part about knowing the theme of our story is that when we do, we know what to leave out.

YOUR STORY MATTERS

Years ago I read a book by Dwight Eisenhower in which he talked about his mother's belief that every child should be raised to understand if they didn't exist their family would fall apart.

Imagine that for a second. Imagine a world in which every person understood they were needed in the world, that they could be the solution to a problem.

Eisenhower is best known for being President, but before he was President he led the troops in World War II, uniting the allies in the fight against Hitler.

And why? It's likely because he was raised to believe the world needed him and even expected something from him.

Do you know the same is true for you? I mean that question literally. Do you know the world needs something from you? Are you intimately aware the positive and negative turns in your life have prepared you to participate in God's effort to save many lives?

There are probably days when you feel like the world would be better off if you stayed in bed but it isn't true. God created you and He created you with the power to bring light into darkness and order into chaos. You are necessary. And the sooner you believe that, the sooner you'll bond with God in living a great story.

The most dangerous person in the world is a person who does not understand how powerful God made them to be. These people recklessly destroy because they think they are invisible and they don't matter. But the sad and happy truth is they do matter. They matter to everybody around them. When we own the seemingly magical nature of our existence, we can be more effective in participating with God to save many lives.

Before you create your Storyline, understand your story matters. Don't play the victim and say "awe shucks" cause to do so is to insult God. You didn't make yourself in your mother's womb, God did, and to say you aren't important is to say his creation lacks substance.

Are you the center of the world? No, but the one who created the world created you as the pinnacle of that creation. Accept this fact and with it the responsibility to live a great story. Lives depend on it.

With that, let's create your Storyline.

LET'S CREATE YOUR STORYLINE

Your Storyline will be a subplot in God's story. As you go through these eight modules, you'll create a life-plan that will ensure you are connected with God and your life is charged with meaning.

MODULE ONE
What Are My Positive and Negative Turns?

All stories are made up of positive and negative turns. As we've seen, even people who walk with God experience suffering. But God can redeem any negative turn so it can be understood as a valuable experience. Finding a redemptive perspective on our negative turns is a pillar in Logotherapy and the Storyline process. Reflecting on a redemptive perspective toward even our darkest tragedies contributes to emotional and psychological wellbeing.

First, though, we must identify the story turns that have taken place in our lives. In module one, we'll reflect on our positive and negative turns.

The rule with a story turn is simple: A story turn is an event that takes place after which the protagonist will never be the same.

Think of a story turn as a doorway. Once you crossed through this doorway, there was no going back.

Story turns are entirely subjective. For some, a seemingly minor event in their lives may have been a story turn, and for others the events were more heavy and monumental.

Here are some examples of story turns:

A positive story turn might be as simple as winning the spelling bee in the fifth grade (the first time you realized you were intelligent) or finding a soul mate.

A negative story turn might involve losing your job, a divorce or, tragically, the loss of a loved one.

A person the age of thirty will have approximately 12 story turns. If you're older, a few more, and if you're younger, a few less.

We've given you space for about thirty.

Let's Get Started...

1. Spend some time reflecting on the major events of your life. Start when you were young and think about experiences in which you suddenly realized more about yourself or about life in general. A story turn might be having met somebody, having experienced a victory or a failure, or having gone through a loss.

2. In the space provided, write down each of your positive and negative turns. Try to put these turns in chronological order but don't worry about specific dates.

3. On the number line next to each turn, circle how positive or negative each turn was on a scale of one to ten, either positive or negative.

Life Turn

(-)   (+)

Title: _____ 10 9 8 7 6 5 4 3 2 1 0 1 2 3 4 5 6 7 8 9 10

Summary: _____

_____

_____

Life Turn

(-)   (+)

Title: _____ 10 9 8 7 6 5 4 3 2 1 0 1 2 3 4 5 6 7 8 9 10

Summary: _____

_____

_____

Life Turn

(-)   (+)

Title: _____ 10 9 8 7 6 5 4 3 2 1 0 1 2 3 4 5 6 7 8 9 10

Summary: _____

_____

_____

Life Turn

(-)   (+)

Title: _____   10 9 8 7 6 5 4 3 2 1 **0** 1 2 3 4 5 6 7 8 9 10

Summary: _____

_____

_____

Life Turn

(-)   (+)

Title: _____   10 9 8 7 6 5 4 3 2 1 **0** 1 2 3 4 5 6 7 8 9 10

Summary: _____

_____

_____

Life Turn

(-)   (+)

Title: _____   10 9 8 7 6 5 4 3 2 1 **0** 1 2 3 4 5 6 7 8 9 10

Summary: _____

_____

_____

Life Turn

(-)   (+)

Title: _____   10 9 8 7 6 5 4 3 2 1 **0** 1 2 3 4 5 6 7 8 9 10

Summary: _____

_____

_____

Life Turn

(-)   (+)

Title: _____   10 9 8 7 6 5 4 3 2 1 **0** 1 2 3 4 5 6 7 8 9 10

Summary: _____

_____

_____

Life Turn

(-)   (+)

Title: _____ 10 9 8 7 6 5 4 3 2 1 **0** 1 2 3 4 5 6 7 8 9 10

Summary: _____

_____

_____

Life Turn

(-)   (+)

Title: _____ 10 9 8 7 6 5 4 3 2 1 **0** 1 2 3 4 5 6 7 8 9 10

Summary: _____

_____

_____

Life Turn

(-)   (+)

Title: _____ 10 9 8 7 6 5 4 3 2 1 **0** 1 2 3 4 5 6 7 8 9 10

Summary: _____

_____

_____

Life Turn

(-)   (+)

Title: _____ 10 9 8 7 6 5 4 3 2 1 **0** 1 2 3 4 5 6 7 8 9 10

Summary: _____

_____

_____

Life Turn

(-)   (+)

Title: _____ 10 9 8 7 6 5 4 3 2 1 **0** 1 2 3 4 5 6 7 8 9 10

Summary: _____

_____

_____

Life Turn

(-)   (+)

Title: _____   10 9 8 7 6 5 4 3 2 1 **0** 1 2 3 4 5 6 7 8 9 10

Summary: _____

_____

_____

Life Turn

(-)   (+)

Title: _____   10 9 8 7 6 5 4 3 2 1 **0** 1 2 3 4 5 6 7 8 9 10

Summary: _____

_____

_____

Life Turn

(-)   (+)

Title: _____   10 9 8 7 6 5 4 3 2 1 **0** 1 2 3 4 5 6 7 8 9 10

Summary: _____

_____

_____

Life Turn

(-)   (+)

Title: _____   10 9 8 7 6 5 4 3 2 1 **0** 1 2 3 4 5 6 7 8 9 10

Summary: _____

_____

_____

Life Turn

(-)   (+)

Title: _____   10 9 8 7 6 5 4 3 2 1 **0** 1 2 3 4 5 6 7 8 9 10

Summary: _____

_____

_____

Life Turn

(-)   (+)

Title: _____   10 9 8 7 6 5 4 3 2 1 0 1 2 3 4 5 6 7 8 9 10

Summary: _____

_____

_____

Life Turn

(-)   (+)

Title: _____   10 9 8 7 6 5 4 3 2 1 0 1 2 3 4 5 6 7 8 9 10

Summary: _____

_____

_____

Life Turn

(-)   (+)

Title: _____   10 9 8 7 6 5 4 3 2 1 0 1 2 3 4 5 6 7 8 9 10

Summary: _____

_____

_____

Life Turn

(-)   (+)

Title: _____   10 9 8 7 6 5 4 3 2 1 0 1 2 3 4 5 6 7 8 9 10

Summary: _____

_____

_____

Life Turn

(-)   (+)

Title: _____   10 9 8 7 6 5 4 3 2 1 0 1 2 3 4 5 6 7 8 9 10

Summary: _____

_____

_____

Life Turn

(-)   (+)

Title: _____   10 9 8 7 6 5 4 3 2 1 **0** 1 2 3 4 5 6 7 8 9 10

Summary: _____

_____

_____

Life Turn

(-)   (+)

Title: _____   10 9 8 7 6 5 4 3 2 1 **0** 1 2 3 4 5 6 7 8 9 10

Summary: _____

_____

_____

Life Turn

(-)   (+)

Title: _____   10 9 8 7 6 5 4 3 2 1 **0** 1 2 3 4 5 6 7 8 9 10

Summary: _____

_____

_____

Life Turn

(-)   (+)

Title: _____   10 9 8 7 6 5 4 3 2 1 **0** 1 2 3 4 5 6 7 8 9 10

Summary: _____

_____

_____

Life Turn

(-)   (+)

Title: _____   10 9 8 7 6 5 4 3 2 1 **0** 1 2 3 4 5 6 7 8 9 10

Summary: _____

_____

_____

MODULE TWO
What is the Theme of My Life?

In module two, you'll transfer your positive and negative turns onto a timeline.

Remember, writers use a visual timeline to help them gain perspective into their characters.

You've already seen two examples of this timeline, one for God's story and the other for the story of Joseph. Now it's time to see your own life in timeline form.

As you create your visual timeline, reflect on each event. Try to remember what your life felt like then.

When you complete your timeline, step back and look at it as a whole. Where has God been in your story?

Many of us will see a theme running through our lives. A theme might be "God was with me" or "God uses me to love people." In the space provided on your timeline, write a theme that you see as a thread through your life. While it may take some reflection, this theme will serve as the first element of the decision filter Storyline will provide.

Let's Get Started...

1. Transfer each of your positive and negative turns onto the timeline. While you'll want to keep the events in chronological order, the spacing between the events doesn't have to be exact.

2. To save space, simply list a title or a few-word summary of each event.

3. Write the name of the event as high above or as low below as its numerical value.

4. When you are done, step back from the timeline and prayerfully consider a theme. If you have trouble coming up with a theme, consider sitting down with some friends to ask for their perspective.

5. If you are going through Storyline as a group or with a counselor, spiritual director or life coach, share your timeline and describe each event as part of the therapuetic process of understanding your story.

"Never will I leave you, never will I forsake you." Hebrews 13:5

(+) Positive Turns

(-) Negative Turns

Theme of My Life:

My Timeline

MODULE THREE

How Can God Redeem My Negative Turns?

Years ago, I was writing a book about growing up without a father. My dad left when I was only two, and I figured since I'd become successful, I should write a book for other fatherless kids.

But the effort backfired. I holed up in a cabin in the San Juan Islands alone for a couple months to work on the book. There in the cabin I discovered I had serious issues to deal with. It was one of the more difficult seasons of my life. I'd walk the shores of the island, thinking about how poorly I'd interacted with women, how irresponsible I'd been in my career and traced much of it back to the fact I never had an intimate, male role model. It was a depressing and lonely time. I made friends with a sea otter and I swear I once had a thirty-minute conversation with him about the merits of Freud's Oedipus complex. I was that lonely.

Nevertheless, I kept writing the book and sought some help from a therapist. A breakthrough came when I was reading an unrelated book about the Truth and Reconciliation Commission in South Africa. Bishop Desmond Tutu was put in charge of a commission to bring healing to his nation after the atrocities of Apartheid. When asked what kinds of people he wanted to serve on the commission, Tutu said he wanted victims. Victims, he said, whose lives had been torn apart. He wanted those who had been raped, who had seen their parents killed, who'd had their houses burned to the ground.

But, he said, they cannot have stayed victims. If they serve on the commission, they must be people who have forgiven their oppressors. These people, Tutu said, will be the wounded healers of South Africa.

When I read that phrase, *wounded healer*, I knew that's what I wanted to be. I wanted to do something meaningful with my pain.

FINDING A REDEMPTIVE PERSPECTIVE BRINGS HEALING

Viktor Frankl famously stated a person can gain a strong sense of meaning when they find a redemptive perspective toward their suffering. What he means by this is in every tragedy we have the ability to find something good. This can be something we've learned, empathy we've gained, or some greater pain somebody has been spared because of our suffering.

Frankl doesn't mean to say tragedy is actually positive. The negative turns in our lives remain negative turns. But if we are going to heal, we must find something meaningful that came to us because of our tragedies.

Frankl tested his theory on more than 30,000 suicidal patients in a hospital system in Vienna and under his watch not a single patient took their lives. Finding a redemptive perspective on our negative turns is an extremely powerful tool in gaining emotional health.

GOD DOES NOT WANT SATAN TO DEFEAT US

God wants to take what Satan has meant for evil and redeem it for His purposes. This is a blow to Satan, to take what he has done in the world, hold it up in his face and say "now look what the Lord has done with your evil work."

God is in the business of redemption. If we want to join Him in His work, we can start by taking our tragedies and allowing them to glorify God in some way.

For me, it was starting a mentoring program. After reading about being a wounded healer, I started an organization that provides mentors for children growing up without fathers. The Mentoring Project is now a large, successful organization that has partnered thousands of kids with mentors. What Satan intended for evil (deceiving my father and wreaking havoc on my family) the Lord redeemed (thousands of kids today have father figures.)

WE ARE NOT VICTIMS

Scripture tells us we are more than conquerors through Him who loved us (Romans 8:37). There is a strong temptation to remain a victim because of the events of our past, but don't fall for it.

Psychologist Henry Cloud defines a victim as a person who is truly powerless in a situation. Many of us were victims when we were children and some of us are victims today. But once we are given the power to redeem a situation, we don't have to be victims anymore. We can participate with God in bringing redemption to our tragedy and light into the darkness.

In module three, we'll attempt to find a redemptive perspective toward our negative turns. This will be one of the most life-giving, health-bringing exercises you'll ever perform.

Another benefit of finding a redemptive perspective on our suffering is that once a tragedy is redeemed, it's difficult for us to consider it a hindrance. Viktor Frankl says it this way: When we find a redemptive perspective toward our suffering, it ceases to be suffering.

YOU WILL FACE RESISTANCE

As we complete this exercise, we'll face resistance. We'll likely want to cling to a victim mindset, or we'll have trouble forgiving somebody who has wronged us.

Victim Mindset: If you're tempted to see yourself as a victim, ask yourself if you're doing so in order to manipulate yourself or others. I know that sounds like a strong, accusatory statement, but honestly ask yourself if you are getting some kind of attention or power from seeing yourself as a victim. If so, prayerfully let go of that identity. It's only causing you more and more pain.

Playing the role of a victim is a powerful way to control others. If we are their victims, they owe us something. But this is a sign of unhealth. In doing this exercise, you may have to prayerfully give up the control you have over others and set them and yourself free.

Trouble With Forgiveness: My friend, Pastor Rick McKinley, once defined forgiveness as accepting the burden somebody has given you while no longer holding anything against them. I liked this definition because it meant we didn't have to be completely healed of something before we offered forgiveness. Forgiveness doesn't mean the pain has gone away, it simply means we relinquish the control we have over the person who has hurt us.

Forgiveness is a process, and while you may not be able to forgive today, begin praying about forgiving those who have wronged you so both you, and they, can be set free.

EXAMPLES OF A REDEMPTIVE PERSPECTIVE

Here are some examples of redemptive perspectives toward our negative turns:

The loss of a job: The loss of our job may have helped us downsize our life. We were humbled through the experience and are realizing what is really important. We may also have been graciously taught our security cannot come from worldly things that are passing, but in God alone.

The loss of a loved one: We came to realize how much our community loved and supported us. We were thankful the person we lost was spared the pain of losing us, and instead we could bear the pain of losing them. The loss helped us realize how short and fragile life is and realigned our priorities.

Again, the idea behind finding a redemptive perspective toward our suffering is not to turn a negative into a positive. A negative turn will always be a negative turn, and trying to be an optimist about a tragedy is annoying.

Rather, what we are trying to do here is to see what God can do with our tragedies. What have we learned? What can now be offered to the world because of our pain? How can this hard thing be redeemed?

*If, after a great deal of reflection, you are still having trouble finding a redemptive perspective on negative turns, consider spending time with a counselor or therapist. We also recommend a program called OnSite in which traumatic events can be discussed in safety with the listening ear of a trained therapist. You can find information about OnSite in the back pages of this guide.

Let's Get Started...

1. Spend some time in prayer. Either take a walk or find a quiet place and ask God to reveal what He'd like to do with the pain you've experienced.

2. Ask yourself honestly if you've been playing the victim in any way. Be tender with yourself, but ask God to help you let go and become more than a conqueror through God's love for you.

3. Use the next few pages to begin reflecting on some of your negative turns and find a redemptive outlook toward each experience.

Negative Turn

Title: _____

Redemptive Perspective: _____

_____

_____

_____

_____

Negative Turn

Title: _____

Redemptive Perspective: _____

_____

_____

_____

_____

Negative Turn

Title: _____

Redemptive Perspective: _____

_____

_____

_____

_____

Negative Turn

Title: _____

Redemptive Perspective: _____

_____

_____

_____

_____

Negative Turn

Title: _____

Redemptive Perspective: _____

_____

_____

_____

_____

Negative Turn

Title: _____

Redemptive Perspective: _____

_____

_____

_____

_____

Negative Turn

Title: _____

Redemptive Perspective: _____

_____

_____

_____

_____

Negative Turn

Title: _____

Redemptive Perspective: _____

_____

_____

_____

_____

Negative Turn

Title: _____

Redemptive Perspective: _____

_____

_____

_____

_____

Negative Turn

Title: _____

Redemptive Perspective: _____

_____

_____

_____

_____

Negative Turn

Title: _____

Redemptive Perspective: _____

_____

_____

_____

_____

Negative Turn

Title: _____

Redemptive Perspective: _____

_____

_____

_____

_____

Negative Turn

Title: _____

Redemptive Perspective: _____

_____

_____

_____

_____

Negative Turn

Title: _____

Redemptive Perspective: _____

_____

_____

_____

_____

Negative Turn

Title: _____

Redemptive Perspective: _____

_____

_____

_____

_____

Negative Turn

Title: _____

Redemptive Perspective: _____

_____

_____

_____

_____

Negative Turn

Title: _____

Redemptive Perspective: _____

_____

_____

_____

_____

Negative Turn

Title: _____

Redemptive Perspective: _____

_____

_____

_____

_____

MODULE FOUR

What Roles Do I Play?

Module four starts the process of creating your Dashboard. From here on, each of the exercises will complete a module on your Dashboard allowing you to see your Storyline at a glance. If you've not already registered to create a Dashboard, do so at **MySubplot.com**.

In this exercise, we will list the roles we play in life. We all wear many hats, but the more clear we are about our roles, the more clear our stories will be. Remember, great stories are **clear**: The protagonist knows who they are, what they want, what resistance they must face and how the story will (hopefully) end.

Clarifying our roles is the first step.

Roles are gifts from God and as such domains of responsibility. When we list our roles, it helps us understand what is expected of us in life.

Not only this, but each of our roles has a separate (or many) Storylines. If a story is a character that wants something and overcomes conflict to get it, we can live many stories at once, depending on how many things we want to accomplish.

When we begin to associate the things we want with God-given domains of responsibility, we add to our decision filter (*Which story am I living that needs a speedboat? The story of my marriage, the story of my career? Hmm, maybe I don't need a speedboat after all...*)

Knowing our roles can keep us from telling meaningless stories with our lives.

DON'T PLAY TOO MANY ROLES

I've never liked long Russian novels because they have too many characters. It's all I can do to keep the names straight.

I've found movies are difficult to follow, too, if there are too many primary characters. Often a movie gets confusing when the lead protagonists aren't clearly defined.

The same can be true in life. When we play too many roles, our story suffers for clarity.

God gives the average person the ability to connect intimately with about twelve people. Some people can connect with more, and some with less but none of us can connect with everybody. We have to choose. The more roles we play in life, the more people depend on us. If we are playing too many roles our lives suffer and so do the lives of those who need our undivided attention.

If you are playing too many roles, people around you may be confused as to what your life is about. And not only this, but you're likely getting burned out.

We have given you space for five roles. You may have more, you may have less, but most of us can only focus on five.

If you are playing too many roles in life, take the time to prayerfully consider dropping a few of those roles. Do you really need to volunteer for the *Evangelical Deforestation Society*? Can we resign from the Board of Directors of *Kittens Against Cat Cancer*? (Nothing against cats, though I'll never understand why anybody would want a pet that won't make eye contact.) Likely not. Let's take the opportunity module four gives us to clean up our stories.

Notes on Roles:

If you break down the idea of roles too far, you quickly realize we play hundreds of roles. In this exercise, though, we are looking for broad and major categories.

It's true your role as a father may encompass five sub categories (depending on how many kids you have), or your role as a leader might encompass ten, but allow these roles to identify broad spectrums of your God-given domains.

Also, if you find you play more than five roles, list the five you feel are most important. You won't be neglecting the rest, you'll just be deciding the five stories you want to focus on first.

** Your Dashboard at **MySubplot.com** allows for an infinite number of stories. We encourage you to use the Dashboard for years to come to plan many stories for each of your roles.*

Let's Get Started...

1. List five roles you play in life by either circling the examples we've provided our adding your roles to the list.

2. If you have more than five roles, prayerfully consider which ones to focus on. Also ask yourself, and God, if there are some roles you need to let go of.

3. Transfer your roles to your Dashboard at **MySubplot.com**

Your Roles (circle five)

Spiritual Being

Husband

Mother

Wife

Father

Sister

Brother

Friend

Business Owner

Leader

Athlete

Artist

Writer

Mentor

Advocate for...

Other: _____

Other: _____

Other: _____

Other: _____

2

A Character
that wants something
and overcomes conflict
to get it.

"Delight yourself in the Lord, and He will give you the desires of your heart."

– Psalm 37:4

"It's stasis that kills you off in the end, not ambition."

– Bono

"A man without ambition is dead. A man with ambition but no love is dead. A man with ambition and love for his blessings here on earth is ever so alive."

– Pearl Bailey

"The world and its desires pass away, but the one who does the will of God lives forever."

– 1 John 2:17

"To the person who does not know where he wants to go there is no favorable wind."

– Seneca

"I can teach anybody how to get what they want out of life. The problem is that I can't find anybody who can tell me what they want."

–Mark Twain

What We Want Determines Our Story

DON'T FEEL GUILTY FOR HAVING DESIRES

There's a wrong idea floating around that we shouldn't have desires. It's a nice sentiment, usually wrapped in language like "I only want to know God more, and nothing else besides…" This all sounds noble and holy but is ultimately unrealistic and counter to God's design.

The truth is God has created us with desires that cannot be exclusively fulfilled in Him. Those who believe God will fulfill all their needs by a relationship with Him are well meaning but theologically confused.

God created us with a need for food and water, but He doesn't become food and water. He created us with a need for community, but He doesn't become multiple people and invite us to go bowling.

In other words, God created us with desires He fulfills through means He provides. Or, better said, all our needs are not met in Christ, though they may be met by Christ.

Whenever a well-meaning twenty-something tells me they aren't going to date until they are fulfilled by their relationship with God, I want to say to them *then you will never date, because God isn't going to show up at your door with flowers. God is God and He will fulfill your God need. If you want a mate, try e-harmony.*

We should not feel guilty or ashamed of having desires. We shouldn't feel guilty about desiring shelter, transportation, food, sex, love, community or even clothes. These are all positive desires.There are also evil desires, and many desires that are good, out of an appropriate context, become evil. In other words, following God is a lot like becoming mature and being able to discern right from wrong, pure from corrupt.

God gives us wisdom and instruction about how to fulfill our desires. There are right ways to fulfill desires and wrong ways. The key, then, is not to stop wanting things but rather to want things and go about the pursuit in a way that honors God.

EVERYBODY MUST PARTICIPATE IN LIFE

Having desires can be scary. If we want things, we could be let down, after all. It might be easier to just not want anything. In fact, there are entire religious systems based on emptying ourselves of desire so we can have peace. But emptying ourselves of desire is not what God wants for us. He created us with desires and we shouldn't ignore them for fear of failure.

I have a friend named Bob Goff who holds a parade on his cul-de-sac every year. He started the parade when his kids were young because he wanted them to have something to do on an otherwise boring New Years Day. The parade became a neighborhood tradition, though, and now hundreds of people march in it. It starts at one end of the street and ends at Bob's house, where they have a barbecue. You can think of it as a glorified block party, if you like.

What makes this parade unique, however, is that nobody gets to watch it. No kidding, everybody has to participate in the parade. Bob has sent me pictures and in each picture there are hundreds of people marching in costumes and holding balloons and yet the curbs are empty. The idea nobody gets to watch the parade came to Bob when he decided it was much more fun to be in the parade than to watch it, so he and the kids stipulated participation. And because everybody had to participate, the neighbors got to know each other and the community bonded through the experience.

I like Bob's parade because it reminds me of the way God designed life. He stipulated everybody must participate. He pulls people off the curb by giving them the need for food, which means they have to hunt and farm, and the need for water which means they couldn't stay in bed all day. He put in men the desire for women, which means they have to shave and take regular showers, and He gave women the desire for men, which is why they bat their eyelashes at Justin Bieber concerts.

God loves participation, and the desires He put in you He put in you for a reason. And the reason is simple: When we participate, we grow. And when we do not participate in life, we do not grow. Immature people are often people who have not been forced to participate in life.

PARTICIPATION IS THE KEY TO MATURITY

Years ago I read a biography about one of my favorite authors. He's a mysterious figure who published only one novel more than fifty years ago. His book was a runaway best seller and still sells thousands of copies today. He only died recently but until his death he holed up in his home and never talked to reporters. He rarely corresponded with fans and built a concrete bunker behind his house where, supposedly, he wrote and wrote, all the while depriving the world of his art.

Everybody has the right to isolate, of course, but few have the luxury. Most of us have to work, which means we have to interact with others. But this writer didn't, and because he didn't, he became odd.

The book talked about how the writer lost the ability to socialize and, when people came around his property, he'd chase them away. Occasionally, even in his old age, he'd begin corresponding with young, high-school girls who wrote requesting interviews for their school papers. It was reported he became perverted and harassed the young girls, often to the point their parents had to get involved. When we don't participate, we suffer. Our growth and maturity depends on getting off the curb and joining the parade. And the way we join the parade is to want something and begin to pursue what we want.

WANTING SOMETHING IS HEALING

Viktor Frankl coined a term *called the existential vacuum*. He speaks of it as a mental state, a kind of morbid depression that suffocates its victims. The existential vacuum comes over somebody when they have nothing to live for, no direction, and no worthwhile reason to get out of bed.

Frankl argued the vacuum came about when we lost our bearings, when society no longer had a way to say what was expected of a human being. Without an expectation, as it were (even a cultural expectation to become a great man or honorable woman) a person is left directionless and has no sense of meaning.

How did Frankl cure those suffering from the existential vacuum? He helped them find a project. He was famous for saying *stop asking what you expect from life, ask what life expects of you.* People who feel life expects something from them are more psychologically healthy than those who don't.

Even those who were the most despondent were given projects. Frankl used the analogy of an arch gaining strength when weight is applied. He said when you give a despondent person a project, they aren't made more weak, they're made more strong. In the hospitals, Frankl began working with those who were suicidal, asking them what good thing they could bring into the world. It wasn't long before those who were once depressed gained hope their lives could have meaning.

YOU WERE DESIGNED TO BE DISTRACTED BY A NOBLE DESIRE

William Wilberforce, Britain's most influential leader in ending the slave trade, clarified his ambitions by saying "God has set before me two great objects, the suppression of the slave trade and the reformation of manners."

Because he identified and clearly marked his ambitions, William Wilberforce lived a fantastic story. Your mind was designed to be distracted by some kind of noble pursuit. We were designed to have domains and territory to steward. Even before the Fall, God gave Adam a job. He told him to name the animals. Did God do this because He couldn't think of names Himself? No, God did this because He'd designed Adam to be a little bit like Him, to be creative and to breathe worlds (or the names of various species) into existence.

Now remember, Adam was walking with God and talking with God and there was no tension between them, and yet Adam was not fulfilled by God alone. He also needed a project, a vision, something to build and create and, well, categorize. God gave Adam a job they could do together as a way of bonding with His creation.

You and I are no different. We need projects to be healthy. We need to have a vision and to breathe something new into the world, whether it's a book, a baby or a model airplane.

When we have a project to work on and a vision to head toward, it's as though we are looking at a philosophical map. We see where we'd like to go and can measure the distance between us and what we want. But if we don't want something, we live in a fog.

If a person's life feels meaningless, it's likely because they live in an existential vacuum where their basic needs are met but they've yet to identify a noble cause to ignite their passions.

EVERY STORY STARTS WITH AN AMBITION

As I mentioned earlier, there's a popular idea in Eastern mysticism that we shouldn't want things. The thinking goes like this: Tension in life is caused when we want things but can't have them, therefore if we stop wanting things, we will live in peace.

That thinking is partly true and it's of noble intent. If nobody wanted anything we wouldn't go to war and neighbors wouldn't fight. The problem is, not wanting anything is the path to a boring life, and it's counter to our design.

I propose we should want things, it's just the things we want should be better.

The better the things we want (I mean things in the in the philosophical sense, not *the things at Bed Bath and Beyond* sense) the better our stories will be.

People who have noble ambitions live inspiring lives. Martin Luther King wanted racial equality and Mother Theresa wanted dignity for the marginalized. Winston Churchill wanted to defeat Hitler (and later Stalin!)

And *what* we want matters. Can you imagine sitting through a movie about a guy who wants a Volvo? At the end of the movie, would you be crying as the guy drove the car off the lot? I doubt it. Because what he wanted wasn't inspiring.

OUR STORIES ARE BEING HIJACKED

Did you know the average American encounters 3,000 commercial messages each day? So 3,000 times per day you're being tempted to want something, whether it's a cup of coffee or a new toaster oven. And when you want something, you're telling a story.

A story begins when a story question is posited. *Will the CIA agent be able to disarm the bomb before it blows up New York City? Will the man who met the beautiful woman on the bus ever meet her again to express his love?*

Pick up any old DVD case and turn it over to read the movie's summary and it'll likely be about a person who wants something and overcomes conflict to get it. Luke Skywalker wanted to defeat the evil empire, Frodo wanted to destroy the ring, Harry wanted Sally.

If your life were summarized on a movie poster, what would it say? Would it say you were trying to pay down your mortgage? Would it say you wanted to buy a larger television?

There's nothing morally wrong with wanting any of that stuff, it's just that it's the stuff of boring stories.

To be sure, I don't care what kind of car you drive or how big your television is (mine's huge) but that can't be what our stories are about.

If we want to tell great stories, we are going to have to want noble things.

WHAT SORT OF THINGS SHOULD WE WANT?

The problem with many people's stories is they die with the protagonist. I mean we might as well throw all our stories in the grave with us because our stuff is going to rust anyway.

But Martin Luther King's story didn't die with him. And neither did Mother Theresa's or the story of William Wilberforce. And yet they died without any stuff at all. Their stories were about the stuff of eternity. Their lives were subplots in a greater epic.

If we want to tell great stories and if we want to participate in what God is doing in the world we need to tell stories about *saving many lives.*

Now this all sounds rather guilt ridden, doesn't it? But I don't mean it that way. I think there's a vision or a project that would save many lives that might ignite your deepest passions.

I remember the first time I went to Africa. I was told the continent would change me, the people would inspire me and I wouldn't come back the same. Well, I loved Africa, truly. And I loved and was inspired by the people. But Africa didn't change me and it didn't ignite my passion. I felt guilty. I felt like a failed humanitarian or something.

When I discovered Storyline, though, I wanted to give up everything I had to do the work. I mean I passed up opportunities to make more money, opportunities to travel and become famous because I'd found my passion, *helping other people find their subplots in God's story.*

BUT DOESN'T GOD HAVE A PLAN FOR OUR LIVES?

I get a little pushback when I talk about this stuff from people who believe God has a specific plan for their lives. As good Christians, they don't want to do their will, they want to do God's will.

The sentiment is noble and should be honored, but I think these people are a little confused.

I don't believe God has a specific plan for most people. I could be wrong, though, because there are several people in the Bible for whom God had a specific plan.

In fact, here's a little checklist so you can know if God has a specific plan for your life.

According to the Bible, you know God has a specific plan for you if:

A.   Your donkey (or any other animal, for that matter) talks to you.
B.   An angel appears before you and wakes you up because he's so bright.
C.   You are a virgin but pregnant.

Where did we get this idea God doesn't speak clearly when He wants something? When I talk to people who believe God has a specific plan for their lives, they act like God is some kind of mystic weirdo talking to them through riddles and we are supposed to use the Bible like a secret decoder ring.

If God has a specific plan for your life, you'll know it because He'll tell you. According to the Bible, it will be very, very clear.

For the rest of us, the scary truth is we get to decide what we want to do with our lives. And we get to decide with God.

GOD IS NOT A CONTROLLING DICTATOR

Imagine you were in college visiting a friend's house for dinner. Now imagine sitting down with your friend's family when the father let everybody know what they were eating, then began telling people what to eat first, then what to drink, then what to say, then what to wear and what job to get and who to marry and so on and so on. Would you think this was a functional or dysfunctional family? I'm hoping you'd think this family was dysfunctional.

Sadly, many Christians see God this way. They see Him as a controlling dictator barking commands down from heaven. These people think of God like a boss and the kingdom of God like a company. They are ever trying to be *profitable for the kingdom of God* for fear they are going to get fired.

But God is not our boss, a dictator or a dysfunctional father. God is perfectly healthy.

I've a picture on my computer of a dad sitting down next to a giant piece of butcher paper. Next to him is his daughter and a box of crayons. When I think about God, I often think of this picture. I see God wanting to do something with us, wanting to create and imagine. I see Him letting us have control of our will and our desires and I see Him bonding with you as the two of you create a new and better world to live in.

I think we are spending a lot of time asking God to tell us what to do when the whole time He's asking us what we'd like to do instead. I think He's asking us what's in our hearts, what makes us come alive, what ignites our passion and *saves many lives.*

Of course, a healthy father guides and disciplines, too. If God asks me what I want to do with my life and I tell him I want to be a photographer at Mardis Gras, He shakes His head and says "No way, buddy."

A guy I know named Garry Friesen wrote a book years ago called *Decision Making and the Will of God*. In the book, Garry shares four principles for decision making and I think they apply for those of us rewriting our stories. Here they are:

• Where God commands, we must obey.
• Where there is no command, God gives us freedom (and responsibility) to choose.
• Where there is no command, God gives us the wisdom to choose.
• When we have chosen what is moral and wise, we must trust the sovereign God to work all the details together for good.

WHAT WE WANT SHOULD SAVE LIVES

When we are talking about saving many lives, the territory is vast. Saving many lives is not just about spreading the gospel or bringing food to the hungry. Saving many lives can be about improving people's marriages, guiding people through sound financial principles or just letting people know they are endowed with basic human dignity.

When James defines true religion, he talks about visiting widows and orphans (James 1:27). Visiting them? Yeah, just heading over and having a conversation, acknowledging their existence and letting them know they matter.

God honors all kinds of ambitions including turning the hearts of people to the fatherless, restoring those who have been marginalized, and fighting for justice.

A life-saving ambition could be as simple as living out a great marriage or adopting a child. God honors ambitions like doing honest business and judging rightly. He wants us to be good stewards of His creation and He wants us to raise children who will know and follow Him.

The key to living a great story is to find that place where your passions and the saving of many lives intersect.

YOU ARE NOT YOUR CAREER

For some, our careers are a large part of our stories, but others of us aren't emotionally connected to our jobs. If that's the case, we should do anything we can to switch careers. However, if that's not possible, don't sweat it. From here on we can think of our jobs as fundraising.

I have a friend who is a lawyer. He sues large construction companies that make crooked sky-scrapers. It's not a *save many lives* kind of job, you know, so he just thinks of his job as a way to get cash to fund his story.

That said, even in his job he's living a great story. He takes on clients for free that can't afford him and even started his own law school to help one kid pass the bar. No kidding. He has his own law school comprised of one student. He found a loophole in some paperwork that allowed him to start a single-student law school. They have sweatshirts and everything.

Don't feel bad about viewing your job as fundraising. Anybody who writes a screenplay has to hit the pavement, hat in hand asking people to invest in their story. It's the same with life. If your job isn't directly connected to saving many lives, consider it fundraising.

Our careers are not our stories. Our stories come from the core of who we are and we are bigger than our jobs. If you are what you do for a living, you are smaller than your potential.

GIVE YOURSELF PERMISSION TO FAIL

The most repeated commandment in scripture is *Do not fear*. It's in the text more than 200 times and it's a good thing too because fear has ruined many great stories.

What keeps most of us from living a great story is a fear of failure. We fear judgment and ridicule so we don't try. But what kind of father would ridicule his kids for failing? Most of the criticism that passes through our brains is untrue and is not the voice of the Father. What's true propels us forward. What's true lets us know we are loved unconditionally. What's true strengthens our faith. We have to discern God's voice and God's voice, more than anything else, says *Do not fear*.

If you have a fear of failure, here's my advice: fail. Seriously, go out and fail five times fast. If you fear rejection from the opposite sex, ask the next person you see on the street to marry you. Get it over with. Discover for yourself you are allowed to fail. When you fail and no leviathan comes out of the ocean to swallow you, you'll realize failure doesn't cost anything significant. What costs you is the fear to try. Everybody loves and respects a person who tries, whether they fail or not. Failure is an education, not a judgment.

MAKE YOUR AMBITIONS CLEAR

One last idea before we get started deciding our ambitions: What we want needs to be clear. If you've ever watched a movie in which you weren't sure what the protagonist wanted, you were likely bored out of your mind. Clarity is critical.

When you know what you want in each of your roles, life suddenly becomes more engaging because we no longer sit in the theater of our mind, looking out our eye holes wondering what's going on.

While building McDonalds, Ray Croc, the company's founder repeated the same motto over and over "Quality, service, cleanliness and value." He kept repeating it for the rest of his life.

When our ambition is clear, we'll know what to do every day of our lives. We may not always want to do it, but we'll know what to do all the same. And so will everybody who works with us and is invested in our story.

Remember, as we build our Storyline we're creating a decision filter. Knowing our roles was the first step, now determining an ambition for each is going to bring our stories to life.

MODULE FIVE
What Do You Want?

The second you decide what you want for each of your ambitions your story will begin. You don't even have to finish the rest of this book (though we recommend it or else you might get bogged down by the coming conflict).

Once you clarify your ambitions your life will make more sense.

The reason for the clarity is because you are a teleological being, that is you were designed to move toward something. Human beings are going somewhere until they die. We go places in our careers and in our relationships. Our body is becoming different as we get older. All things are changing and nothing is static.

Anything static is dead and any mind that doesn't know clearly where it is going is dying psychologically. One of the most healing things you can do in your life is to point toward a distant horizon and say to yourself *I will go there.*

To be sure, the healing isn't in the arriving, but in the going. Again, if we aren't *going*, we are dying.

THE EXISTENTIAL VACUUM

In the luxurious west we have most of the things we need, so it's possible to not really want anything. Again, when food, water, shelter and sex are at hand, we are left to decide for ourselves what we should pursue.

America is a country caught in an existential vacuum. In the absence of needs, we are left to decide what we want, and those wants have been hijacked by commercialism. As such, we want a new car or new house or new clothes, all the stuff of boring stories. It's no wonder so many people feel like their lives are meaningless.

Once a person chooses a noble ambition, however, the existential vacuum will collapse and they will return, in part, to emotional stability.

WHY ARE CLEAR AMBITIONS HEALING?

You were not designed to sit around and look at your belly button. You were designed to be distracted (interested and compelled) by something outside yourself. This is why the feeling of love is so pleasant, because it finally frees us from thinking about ourselves all the time.

Not only this, but when we decide we want something, we enter into a story.

Story works like a riddle in that a good story posits a story question: *Will the CIA operative disarm the bomb?* or *Will the lead character be able to save his marriage?*

The reason we love movies is because they posit a question that peaks our curiosity. When our curiosity is peaked we stick around to get the answer and in doing so we are thinking about the question and not about ourselves. People watch television and movies to get their minds off themselves.

So imagine living a life with a compelling story question. Imagine waking up in the morning and caring about your story more than your own depression or circumstances.

When you decide you want something, you automatically posit a story question and become more engaged in an adventure than your own neurosis.

One of the keys to emotional health is to get lost in something greater than yourself.

Once we launch our story we will be living in a page turner. We will wake each morning trying to make something happen and we'll wonder whether we can get it done. Once you launch your story you'll be like Rudy wondering whether he'll make the football team or Jerry McGuire hoping he can create a better sports agency.

In module five you're going to decide an ambition for each of your roles.

Here are some tips:

1. Pray over each of your roles. Take time to get alone and ask God to help you figure out an ambition to ignite your passion.

2. Consider everything a rough draft. As you fill out your Dashboard at **MySubplot.com** know you can always make changes. In fact, count on writing down some ambitions that "don't stick" in your effort to discover your heart.

3. Ask yourself how each ambition will *save many lives*. Is each ambition serving somebody other than yourself? If so, how? Your story doesn't have to be as big as Joseph's, but if you want it to be meaningful it should positively affect others.

4. Consider your first set of stories "practice stories." If you don't quite know what you want in life, consider running a marathon or renewing your vows. Consider going on a short vacation with one of your kids or renting canoes and floating a river. Consider auditioning for a play or writing a book of poems. If you haven't married an ambition yet, by all means date a few to see which ambitions might last in the long run.

5. Don't forget, you are free to fail. The healing is not in the arriving, it's in the journey. Just point to the horizon and start moving. At some point, you may find a place on another horizon you'd rather go. But sooner or later, your whole heart will be involved in the journey. For now, just get moving.

Here are a couple examples of ambitions that make for great stories:

ROLE	AMBITION
Husband	I want my wife to feel supported by my being present as I take time away from work to bond with her, listen to what's going on in her life and show my love by going on walks, engaging in monthly outings and learning more about her story.
Business Owner	I want my employees to have clear, positive direction and support both emotionally and in terms of resources. I want to check in with my principle team members once a month to find out what's going on in their lives and what they need from me. I want to prepare the next generation of leadership within our organization by identifying three new leaders and mentoring them to represent the organization well.

Let's Get Started...

1. List your five primary roles.

2. Prayerfully consider an ambition for each role that might ignite your passions.

3. Summarize your ambitions for each role and write your ambition in the space provided. Consider these pages a rough draft.

4. Transfer your ambitions to your Dashboard at **MySubplot.com** and continue to edit them as needed.

* On your Dashboard, you'll be able to plan as many stories as you like.

ROLE	AMBITION

ROLE	AMBITION
	What do you want?
	What do you want?
	What do you want?

MODULE SIX
Creating Inciting Incidents

Now that we have some ambitions written down, we'll need help to achieve them.

Remember your New Years resolutions? How'd you do? Most of us start the year with great intentions but have trouble following through. I figure we've got as much of a chance making our ambitions happen as we did achieving our New Years resolutions. Intentions are nice, but intentions never built a bridge or saved a marriage.

Thankfully, though, there's something we can do to *make ourselves* follow through.

There's a principle in screenwriting that is also true in life and it's this: people don't want to change.

Change is frightening because it throws us into a mystery. Even people who are living boring lives fear change because their boring lives are predictable. For some, the only thing more frightening than a predictably boring life is a life in which they don't know what will happen. This is one of the reasons people stay with abusers. *Better the devil you know* and all that...

But this will not do. Knowing we are likely to stay in our comfortable and predictable lives, we need to do something to force action.

At the beginning of most stories we see a character at peace with the world. He's at peace for about ten minutes and then something happens that makes him get off the couch. Either he gets bit by a dog or framed for a crime or the plane she's on gets hijacked. This event, right at the beginning of the story, is called an *inciting incident.*

The point of the inciting incident is to throw the protagonist into a state of disharmony, and it's a powerful tool to change a human life.

HUMANS MOVE FROM DISHARMONY TO HARMONY

Once a character is in disharmony they are suddenly motivated. A human will not be motivated to change until their life is in disharmony. So if you want to get yourself off the couch, you've got to create an inciting incident that will force you to get up.

In stories, if somebody kidnaps the protagonist's kid they are thrown into disharmony and motivated to take action.

If the protagonist meets a beautiful girl, they will be in disharmony until they see her again. You'll start seeing this in movies now. About fifteen minutes into almost every film, something will happen that throws the main character into disharmony.

Again, the idea of an inciting incident is simply this: Disrupt the comfort of the protagonist's world so they will be motivated to action.

Because people like to be comfortable the story question is always the same: *Will the character resolve the tension so they can return to a peaceful state?*

INCITING INCIDENTS IN REAL LIFE

We don't recommend kidnapping your friend's kids in order to get them off the couch, but in real life inciting incidents can be just as powerful.

An inciting incident might be signing up for a half marathon or quitting your job. You might register for flight school or agree to finance the drilling of a well in Africa.

An inciting incident is different from an ambition. Many people confuse the two. An ambition can be vague, but an inciting incident must be specific. An ambition might be theoretical while an inciting incident must be based in action.

For instance, a person might have the ambition to get into shape. That's pretty vague and not very motivating. In order to get themselves off the couch, though, an inciting incident might involve signing up for a class to become a Yoga instructor. You see, the inciting incident is a physical act, it's a doorway through which we can never return. An inciting incident **forces action**.

If a guy wanted to rekindle the lost love in his marriage, he might hire an artist to illustrate a book of poems he intends to secretly write. Whatever the inciting incident is, it must force the character to take action and is itself an action.

I had a friend years ago who wanted to be a singer/songwriter. He was a good guitar player and wrote great songs but did little except talk about his ambitions. Tired of hearing him talk about his ambitions but not following through, I booked a local venue, grabbed a picture of him off the internet and posted concert posters all over town. He was suddenly thrust into a story. He could either not show up at the concert or start practicing!

Remember, the idea behind an inciting incident is to disrupt our otherwise comfortable lives. Without this disruption, it's unlikely we will act on our ambitions.

Here are some examples of inciting incidents:

ROLE	AMBITION	INCITING INCIDENT
Husband	I want my wife to feel supported by my being present as I take time away from work to bond with her, listen to what's going on in her life and show my love by going on walks, engaging in monthly outings and learning more about her story.	I will take Fridays off for the next two months and book travel for two weekend outings to reconnect with my wife.
Business Owner	I want my employees to have clear, positive direction and support both emotionally and in terms of resources. I want to check in with my principle team members once a month to find out what's going on in their lives and what they need from me. I want to prepare the next generation of leadership within our organization by identifying three new leaders and mentoring them to represent the organization well.	I'll invite potential new leadership over to the house for dinner on Thursday of next week. I'll plan a weekend at my friend's cabin in which I take my team leaders fishing and explain my vision, giving them direct responsibility for various aspects of the plan.

THE *WHAT IF?* GAME

Coming up with inciting incidents is a creative exercise. Some people are more creative than others so to stimulate ideas you might want to play a little game. If you're doing Storyline as a small group or with your life coach or spiritual director, get out a white board and have some fun with this one.

When writers struggle with a story turn, they often play the *What if?* game. The *What if?* game is simple, really. All you need to do is get out a piece of paper (or use the space we've provided in this book) and ask the question *What if?*

Here are the rules of the game:

1.   Ask *What if?* I did such and such? as it relates to each of your ambitions.
2.   Do not judge or filter your *What if?* answers.
3.   Do not think you have to act on any of your *What if?* answers.
4.   Do not censor your *What if?* questions.

The idea behind the *What if?* game is to free your thinking. Is your ambition to start a non-profit? Your *What if?* questions might go something like this: *What if I built a website? What if I asked Tina Fey to be my spokesperson? What if I quit my day job? What if I filed for tax-exempt status? What if I sent out a support letter? What if I came up with a logo and printed it on a t-shirt?*

Each of these suggestions would certainly get the ball rolling, though some of them are more realistic than others.

Regardless, once you play the *What if?* game you'll have a list of potential ideas for inciting incidents. And you'll likely find something peculiar will happen. A few days from now, one of those ideas won't seem so crazy, and a few days later, it'll start to seem realistic. And a month from now you'll be quitting your job, filing for a tax exempt status and Tina Fey will be wearing your t-shirt!

Let's Get Started...

1. Use the column on the next page to play the *What if?* game. You might want to start the game on a blank sheet of paper or a white board and use the space we've provided for more realistic ideas. (See example on this page.)

2. Narrow down your list into inciting incidents you can actually do and use the Inciting Incident column as your rough draft.

3. Prayerfully consider whether to take action. Seek the counsel of others, but remember, great stories involve risk. In no way are you ensured things will work out, but God doesn't care if you fail.

4. Once you have a list of inciting incidents, take action. Consider this a to-do list so that over the next month you get moving within each of your stories. On your Dashboard, each of your inciting incidents will have a check mark next to it so you can check them off when you follow through. That checkbox is intentional. It is designed to haunt us until we check it.

Remember, to make a story happen the character has to do something. It's time to jump into a better story.

ROLE	*WHAT IF?*	INCITING INCIDENT
Athlete	I opened a yoga studio I signed up for a marathon I filmed a youtube series of exercise videos I wrote a cookbook I challenged Michael Phelps to a race	To sign up for a marathon To take a yoga class

ROLE	WHAT IF?	INCITING INCIDENT
1	?!	
2	?!	
3	?!	
4	?!	
5	?!	

3
A Character
that wants something
and overcomes conflict
to get it.

"I have told you these things so that in me you may have peace. In this world you will have trouble, but take heart. I have overcome the world."
- John 16:33

"Character cannot be developed in ease and quiet. Only through experience of trial and suffering can the soul be strengthened, ambition inspired, and success achieved."
– Helen Keller

"That is why, for Christ's sake, I delight in weakness, in hardships, in persecutions, in difficulties. For when I am weak, then I am strong."
- 2 Corinthians 12:10

"Now I want you to know, brothers, that what has happened to me has really served to advance the gospel. As a result, it has become clear throughout the whole palace guard and to everyone else that I am in chains for Christ. Because of my chains, most of the brothers in the Lord have been encouraged to speak the word of God more courageously and fearlessly."
- Philippians 1:12-14

Great Subplots Include Lots of Conflict

CONFLICT IS GOOD

Conflict is a storyteller's best friend. Conflict is what makes a story engaging and the more conflict you get your character into the less likely people will be to nod off in their popcorn.

If there's no conflict characters can't be made to change and the protagonist won't value their accomplishments. And besides that, without conflict Frodo wouldn't have anything to do. Come to think of it, without conflict, we wouldn't either.

Viktor Frankl says it this way: "Pathology does not only result from stress but also from a relief from stress which ends in emptiness. Lack of tension as it is created by the loss of meaning is as dangerous a threat in terms of mental health as is too high a tension."

As I said before Fankl also proposed suffering ceases to be suffering when we understand it from a redemptive perspective.

I want to convince you that while conflict can be difficult and even painful, much of conflict also serves us. Conflict, along with our ambitions, will keep us from focusing on ourselves and thinking only of ourselves is akin to pathology.

But that doesn't make conflict fun. It's not fun. It's just good. Here are a few reasons why.

CONFLICT IS THE ONLY WAY A PERSON CHANGES

There's an absolute, die-hard rule in screenwriting: The only way to change a character is to put them through hell.

The world's leading story expert, Robert McKee says the only way you can turn a jerk into a nice guy is through conflict. Conflict is the only way to make a weak man strong, a frightened woman brave, an arrogant person humble and a selfish person altruistic.

Characters do not change when they are content. It's true in story and it's true in life.

If I wrote a story about a character that went through a dramatic transformation without having to go through conflict nobody would believe me. They'd throw the book across the room out of sheer frustration. Intuitively, everybody knows people only change under pressure. You may not have realized it until now, but it's a fact of life.

Some might argue joy changes us as much as conflict but it isn't true. Joy is something we feel when we've conquered our conflict. But joy isn't what changed us, it was the conflict that changed us.

CONFLICT LENDS VALUE TO THAT WHICH WE ATTAIN

Years ago I was hiking in the Andes Mountains of Peru. I needed to lose some weight so I created an inciting incident to take a four-day trek that involved climbing over a fourteen-thousand foot mountain pass. I trained for months and lost twenty pounds preparing. Still, the hike was brutal. It turns out the going up wasn't the problem, it was the coming down. To this day, I've never been in more pain. We were dehydrated from the trek and on the second to last day had to descend nine miles down stone steps, many of which were two and three feet tall. We began the day's hike before sunrise and ended it by flashlight. By the time we made camp, I walked into the shower without removing my clothes. I was too tired to undress.

Our trek followed the sacred trail and ended at the lost city of Machu Picchu. I'll never forget the first day of the climb, though, when our guide, Carlos, took us to the edge of a plateau to show us a diverging path. We were only a few miles in and eager and feeling pretty good when he told us there was another path, a path that followed the river and if we wanted, we could take it all the way to the lost city. We'd be there in only six hours, Carlos told us, and the trail was flat and cooled by the river.

But seniors *y senoritas*, he said, *we will not take this path. Instead, we will arrive at the lost city four days from now, and we will climb into those mountains.* Carlos turned and pointed toward the snow-capped Andes, many of them towering over twenty-one thousand feet, nearly seven thousand feet taller than any mountain in Colorado and only five thousand feet shorter than Everest.

The Inca, Carlos said, would only let commercial goods come into the city by the easier trail. Everybody on a spiritual pilgrimage had to pass through the mountains. *Do you know why they demanded spiritual pilgrims pass through the mountains?* Carlos asked.

Because they wanted people to appreciate the city when they got there, he said. *And the pain of this trek will bring out the beauty of the lost city.*

It's true what Carlos said. We spent four days in those mountains and when we got to the lost city, I could swear it was more beautiful to us than to those who'd come by bus. It is, to this day, one of the most beautiful sights I've seen. And I'm convinced it had more to do with the pain of the journey than the steep green hills or the remnants of a lost civilization enshrined amongst the clouds.

Some of our ambitions will be difficult, but be thankful for the challenges. They may hurt in the moment, but when we look back, the pain will add meaning to the story and joy to the celebratory ending.

Have you ever wondered why men and women are so different, why they find it so hard to communicate? Perhaps the reason is God actually embeds conflict into that which He wants us to fight for.

SOME CONFLICT IS INTENDED BY GOD

If we think conflict is something that only came about because of the Fall of Man, we're wrong. Certainly more conflict came into the world at the Fall, but conflict predated the unfortunate eating of the apple.

When I talk about conflict here I'm talking specifically about a sense of incompleteness and a kind of negative emotional state. Indeed, when I talk about conflict before the Fall of Man, I'm talking about a form of suffering.

We are often taught if we have a right relationship with God we'll be at peace and know no discomfort, but this isn't true.

When Adam walked and talked and had intimacy with God he was not complete. He needed a helpmate and felt this need in the form of loneliness or a sense life wasn't quite what it should be. The Bible says Adam could not find a helpmate suitable, which insinuates a feeling of being incomplete, which is of course a negative emotion.

I've heard it said we can be *made complete in God*, but we can't. As mentioned before in this book, God created us with other needs besides Himself and each of those needs can be considered an inciting incident that launches us into a story or forces us to participate in the parade.

Adam had a need for a woman. And because there were no women, he had a feeling of incompleteness. But it's worse than you might think. It's not like Adam met Eve and forgot to get her phone number. Women didn't exist. He had a longing and yet couldn't possibly imagine anything that might fulfill this longing. The only gender option on Facebook was *Male*.

So what did God do about Adam's conflict? He created Eve, right? Actually, that's not what He did at all. Rather than relieving Adam of his frustrations, God ramped up the conflict. Just after God acknowledged Adam couldn't find a helpmate suitable, God gave him a job, an ambition, if you will. He told Adam to *name the animals*. (Genesis 2:20)

Now that really stinks!

Here's a guy who is starving for the company of a gender he can't imagine, and God gave him a job naming animals.

And this was no small task, either. It was a long trek through the Andes. It was mountain pass after mountain pass. We've reduced the story of Adam to a children's story, but there's nothing childish about it. Adam was more like Darwin on the Galapagos Islands, categorizing species and likely working with God to create broad categories and specific names and definitions.

I met a guy once who was trying to name the unnamed species. Did you know there are more than twenty-million unnamed species on the planet today? It's true. There's a consorted effort from scientists around the world to create a Wikipedia of the species and the project will take thousands of people dozens of years to complete.

So when Adam was told to name the species the project likely took him between ten and one-hundred years. If he only named broad categories, the process would have been shorter, but if he had to get specific, we're talking about a giant chunk of his lifetime.

And why?

The moment Adam completed his job, God put the man to sleep and took from his side a rib which he fashioned into a woman.

God made Adam take the long route through the mountains for one reason: So he'd value Eve.

We value more that which we have to work to attain, and we devalue almost anything that comes easy.

When Adam woke and saw Eve the author captures Adam's sentiments in the form of a Hebrew poem. Adam says:

Bone of my bone and flesh of my flesh.

What he's saying here is *She's like me.*

Having studied animal after animal, Adam couldn't find a helpmate suitable. The dogs were a nice companion, the monkeys were entertaining, but his heart longed for more. At last, he said, God provided.

I am convinced, then, God embeds conflict into our lives. I think He does this to build our character, but also so we will appreciate His provision.

And don't forget, God also put Adam through conflict to benefit Eve. Adam appreciated her more because of the conflict he went through before being given her as a companion.

Consider now how hard it is to start a career, sustain a family, build a house, write a song or finish a book. There's nothing easy about our work, but when we understand the conflict serves us, our attitude can radically change and we can embrace conflict rather than avoid it.

The most crippling belief a person can have is *life was supposed to be easy.* Can you imagine how much more painful life would be if you thought life was hard because you were doing something wrong?

Conflict isn't what detracts from our wellbeing. Conflict is great. What detracts from our wellbeing is the thought we weren't supposed to be experiencing conflict in the first place.

GOD CAN REDEEM ALL CONFLICT

Not all conflict is intended by God, but all conflict is allowed by God. Because God is not controlling (His loving nature lets his creation have free choices) people often do things that break God's heart. You've no doubt been the victim of the sins of others. And you've no doubt hurt others with your sin.

This is a terrible reality and God hates it. And yet He can work to redeem it. What Satan intended for evil, God can use for good.

As we write our stories, we will encounter dark realities. As we discussed earlier when we worked to redeem our negative turns, always remember God can redeem even the hardest of situations.

God wants us to redeem conflict. He wants us to display courage and hope in the midst of challenge. He wants us to be humble and allow conflict to change our character. And He wants us to conquer conflict, to tame it and bring order into chaos.

GOD CALLS US INTO CONFLICT

The average American encounters 3,000 commercial messages each day, and because of this we've been programmed to think life was supposed to be easy. It isn't. Life is supposed to be meaningful and we can't gain a sense of meaning without conflict.

When Jesus asks people to follow Him, He's asking them to enter into a challenging, counter-intuitive life. When Jesus says *I have come to give you life more abundantly,*

He's not talking about a life of comfort, He's talking about a life of meaning. He's calling us to the challenge of following Him, a challenge so purposeful and hopeful that suffering for His sake becomes a reward.

If we think of Jesus as a product that promises a comfortable life we will always feel God is letting us down. But the problem isn't that He's not doing what He promised, the problem is we misunderstood what He meant by an *abundant life.*

Jesus is not a product that will make life perfect, He's a living being that wants a relationship and relationships are hard.

Can you imagine the Apostle Paul, doing an infomercial for the product of Jesus?

There he is on late-night television, pitching the product of Jesus, talking about how much the product has changed his life.

"Hi, I'm Paul and I want to tell you about the product of Jesus. I used to have a job and money and friends and lots of power. And then I got the product of Jesus and lost my job, my friends, my money and my power. Today, I'm secretly shuffled from town to town where I'm routinely ridiculed, imprisoned, tortured and occasionally bitten by snakes. You too can have the product of Jesus by calling 1-800…"

There could even be a doctors warning at the end of the infomercial: *The product of Jesus may cause temporary blindness. If your blindness lasts more than three days seek medical attention.*

Jesus asks us to take up our cross and follow Him. That's conflict.

CONFLICT NEEDS A NARRATIVE CONTEXT

I know it all sounds scary but the truth is we like conflict more than we think. When I was training to climb Mt. Hood, recently, I liked hiking up into the clouds each week. And I liked the feeling I had when I got back to the car, my muscles sore from spending a few hours on the trail.

Marathoners may look miserable, but they run those races because they like to. For whatever reason, they like the pain.

Ever heard a great story about how hard a guy had to work to pursue his wife? The harder he worked the better the story. Did he have to ride his bike to the next town every day? Did he have to fight off some other guy? It doesn't matter, he loved doing it and he loves telling the story because the conflict displays how much he loves his wife.

Conflict hurts the most when it doesn't have a narrative context. The Apostles suffered for Jesus because they loved Him and they wanted to participate in what He was doing. With the right narrative context you'll quit your job, swim the English channel, fast for a month, face your fears and fight the enemy. Conflict makes life worth living. Without it we'd be bored.

There's nothing so miserable as enduring pain without a narrative context. Put me on a mountain and point me toward the summit and suddenly being pelted with rain and ice feels like an exhilarating challenge. If you sit me on the couch and throw ice chunks at me, though, the pain is less satisfying.

The sad truth is life is full of pain and without a worthy ambition, we are sitting on the proverbial couch, taking the pain without a worthwhile context. That sounds like a miserable life. We need to give our conflict a narrative context in order to redeem it.

We are going to experience conflict whether we are living a story or not. Might as well have a narrative context so the pain makes sense and contributes to a life of meaning.

A NARRATIVE CONTEXT GIVES REASON TO HOLINESS

If we aren't participating with God in saving many lives, resisting sin is nearly impossible. We need a narrative context within which to face our challenges. When we are righteous for the sake of a vision, our conflict becomes a challenge rather than a burden.

I have a friend who said to me, *you know, Don, the Bible makes a lot more sense when you are actively following Jesus. If you just study it at rest, it's really hard to make sense of it. But out in the field, out in the trenches, it's life, it's fresh water, it's food for the soul.*

CONFLICT IS RESISTANCE

We may have to do some serious reflection and submission when it comes to accepting conflict as part of life. The Bible talks about *fighting the good fight* (1 Timothy 6:12) and *running the race set before us* (Hebrews 12:1) and so we shouldn't think the idea of embedded conflict is foreign to God. When we know conflict is coming and anticipate it, and when we know God is our coach and our guide and is *for us*, the conflict becomes a noble challenge.

Remember, Steven Pressfield says when something beautiful is trying to come into the world it will face an equal and opposite resistance. This is true for every creative project and it will be true if we try to live a better story.

Resistance has many forms. As we try to live a great story we'll face criticism, doubt and no small amount of distraction. But we've got to keep our feet moving. Every day that isn't a rest day means we lower our shoulders and push the plot another inch toward the climactic scene.

Writing coach William Zinsser says *writers love to have written*. As a writer, I identify completely. There's nothing more grueling than sitting down to the blank page. For whatever reason, I'd rather watch television or mow the lawn or even go for a hike than sit down and work on a book.

My friend Justin Zoradi runs an organization called *These Numbers Have Faces*. In his work, he provides scholarships for students in second and third-world countries so students can attend college. Each of his students then pays back their scholarship through community service that helps somebody else. It's a revolutionary program and under Justin's leadership it's thriving.

I talked with Justin recently and he said something I'll remember for years. Justin said: *Don, just sitting down to do my job every day is a revolutionary act. It may not feel like it, but by showing up at the office and facing the mundane nature of the work, I'm pushing back against academic inequality. I get up, I do my work.*

I loved that attitude. Justin inspires me and while it may not feel like it your story matters and your work matters, too.

I agree with Justin in that when we push the plot forward we'll drive light into darkness, no matter how mundane it may feel. If we're telling a good love story with our spouse, we're sparing the world another lonely heart and we're proving we do have some agency in making love happen. We may not feel like picking up flowers that day or taking another hour to listen, but in doing so we are a revolutionary fighting darkness. And it's this way with our work and our children and our friendships, too. In real life, there's no dramatic music playing in the war scenes, it's just mud and trenches and bullets and blood. But make no mistake, those mundane moments in which we show up and push the plot forward are eternally powerful and significant.

When we take up our cross to follow Christ (Luke 9:23) it means giving up that business opportunity to spend time with our kids, it means sitting and listening to our spouse, it means going on that mission trip, it means giving a portion of our money to the church, it means taking action on the things we don't feel like doing.

In the end, it won't matter what we felt, it will only matter what we did. This means our moods don't have to dictate our stories. Our actions dictate our stories.

WE HAVE NO REASON TO FEAR

Living great stories means entering into a world of risk and fear. If you're conflict avoidant, this is going to be tough, but press on. Keep pushing your story a little further outside your comfort zone.

Jesus Himself faced an intense amount of conflict. Imagine the storms brewing in His soul the night before He was crucified. There He was in the garden, connecting with the Father through prayer and even those closest to Him fell asleep. He knew He'd have to die, and He knew the tortuous way in which He'd been asked to redeem the world. He even asked if there could be any other way. The text doesn't say Jesus was afraid, but any sane person would be. And yet He was consumed by love. He loved us and He loved the Father. He moved through the place where fear would collapse most men and his ambition conquered the conflict.

Over 200 times in Scripture the text says *Do not fear*. This is the most often repeated command in Scripture. And we must obey. If we do not consistently face fear, we aren't following God. God takes light into the dark places, and so must we.

John A. Shedd reminds us a ship at harbor is safe, but that's not what ships are for. Look at yourself in the mirror and tell me you weren't designed for an adventure. I know it's scary, but think about your passions and your desires and your longings. Weren't you made to just go a little farther than your fear suggests? Living a good story isn't safe, but it's meaningful. Face your fear. Conquer it. And if it conquers you, show it how it didn't end you. Get up and live another great story.

Remember what Justin said: Showing up every day is a revolutionary act. Let's show up to life. Let's prove how beautiful it can really be. Let's face the conflict, redeem it, conquer it, and allow it to mold our character. Let's participate in what God is doing in the world.

MODULE SEVEN
Anticipating Conflict

Now that you've decided your ambitions and created a few inciting incidents, conflict is going to knock at your door. Soon you may be cursing this book. It all sounded so romantic at first, didn't it? Quitting your job, signing up for a marathon, harboring a litter of baby coyotes in your condo. But there's nothing fun about wondering how you're going to pay the bills or the incessant howling of coyote's every time there's a full moon (trust me I know.)

I'm hoping you're convinced by now conflict can be good. I promise, it will serve your story. And half the frustration of conflict goes away when you anticipate it. It's when we think we aren't supposed to experience conflict that it hurts.

You'll be amazed the next time you get into a disagreement with your spouse about how much easier things go when you realize marriages are supposed to be challenging. They are challenging by design, as are children, careers and creative projects. Again, *saving many lives* isn't supposed to be easy, it's supposed to be meaningful.

As we move forward in creating our Storylines, we want to anticipate what kind of conflict we'll encounter for each of our ambitions. There are two reasons to do this, the first is so we won't be blindsided, and the second is because we want to reflect on the redemptive aspects of the conflict we will endure.

When you fight with your husband, spend time reflecting on the redemptive aspects of dealing with somebody different than yourself. Is the process humbling, is the process character building? Finding any kind of redemptive perspective on our conflict redeems it and makes it bearable.

Let's Get Started...

1. For each of your roles, list the conflict you'll likely face as you head toward your ambition. We've given you a list of categories to stimulate your reflection, but feel free to list any conflict you anticipate outside these categories.

2. Enter the conflict you anticipate in your online Dashboard at **MySubplot.com.**

3. Make sure to edit as you go. Every time you enter a new anticipated conflict, you're reminding yourself conflict can be a meaningful part of life when it has a narrative context. Within a short period of time, your attitude toward conflict will change.

4. For each new area of conflict you enter on your Dashboard, consider a redemptive perspective as a way of "taking the sting" out of the challenges you will face.

ANTICIPATED CONFLICT FOR ROLE 1

Physical Challenges:

Characteristics I Need to Develop:

Financial Challenges:

Skill Deficiencies:

Relational Complications:

How are These Conflicts Redemptive?

Other:

ANTICIPATED CONFLICT FOR ROLE 2

Physical Challenges:

Characteristics I Need to Develop:

Financial Challenges:

Skill Deficiencies:

Relational Complications:

How are These Conflicts Redemptive?

Other:

ANTICIPATED CONFLICT FOR ROLE 3

Physical Challenges:

Characteristics I Need to Develop:

Financial Challenges:

Skill Deficiencies:

Relational Complications:

How are These Conflicts Redemptive?

Other:

ANTICIPATED CONFLICT FOR ROLE 4

Physical Challenges:

Characteristics I Need to Develop:

Financial Challenges:

Skill Deficiencies:

Relational Complications:

How are These Conflicts Redemptive?

Other:

ANTICIPATED CONFLICT FOR ROLE 5

Physical Challenges:

Characteristics I Need to Develop:

Financial Challenges:

Skill Deficiencies:

Relational Complications:

How are These Conflicts Redemptive?

Other:

4

A Character that wants something and overcomes conflict **to get it.**

"And if I go and prepare a place for you, I will come back and take you to be with me that you also may be where I am." (John 14:3)

"His master replied, 'Well done, good and faithful servant! You have been faithful with a few things; I will put you in charge of many things. Come and share your master's happiness!' (Matthew 25:23)

"It is very dangerous to go into eternity with possibilities which one has oneself prevented from becoming realities. A possibility is a hint from God. One must follow it."
–Soren Kierkegaard

"Don't part with your illusions. When they are gone, you may still exist, but you have ceased to live." –Mark Twain

Great Subplots Head Toward Climactic Scenes

CLIMACTIC SCENES ARE MORE MOTIVATING THAN GOALS

Your brain doesn't work like a computer. If you put a human brain on a table next to a computer you'd notice they look different. A computer looks nice and clean but a brain looks like a pile of worms. And they function just as differently. If you've spent years trying to download information about nutrition, relationships, spirituality and career into your brain but can't seem to get your "self" to change it's because you've been treating your mind like a computer. It's not. The human brain was designed to connect with people, to live within the context of a narrative and to connect with God. Computers are just digital slaves. You're not a slave. You're a living being.

If we want to change our minds, we have to do so holistically. We have to get off the couch and change the way we live because how we live is who we become. We have to live great stories if we want to become great people.

STORIES CHANGE HOW OUR BRAINS ENGAGE LIFE

I mentioned earlier that several years ago I needed some motivation to get fit. I'd set goals to lose weight and hit the gym and all that, but without a narrative context my goals were powerless.

From my living room window in Portland, though, I looked out every day at all 11,000 feet of Mt. Hood. It's not a big mountain when you compare it to peaks around the world, but what makes Mt. Hood majestic is you view it from sea level. It comes out of the foothills like a skyscraper in a row of mobile homes.

I'd had friends who'd climbed Mt. Hood before and I'd always dreamed of summiting it myself. And that's when I came up with the idea to forego the gym for a better story. I was going to summit Mt. Hood.

I used the inciting incident of asking friends in Texas if they wanted to join me and they did, so we got on a training routine. About once a week I'd head to the Columbia River Gorge to hike Dog Mountain, a slightly grueling five-mile trek a lot of the locals use to train for their Hood attempts.

I was motivated by the climactic scene I envisioned. I imagined making that final push with my friends, all of us roped to each other and anchored to the mountain, passing through the clouds to stand at the highest point in Oregon. I don't think an hour went by when I wasn't imagining that scene. It began to consume me and it kept me on task.

A goal is usually a statistic, a number of pounds or an amount of money in our savings account. Goals are great, but they're dead. Climactic scenes are living and moving and, most importantly, come alive within the context of a narrative.

Sadly, my friends and I never summited Mt. Hood. We tried for two weeks but in each attempt were turned back by weather. We'd slog up the mountain being pelted by rain and ice only to turn back after a few hours work. Nevertheless, we had a great time trying and each of us were in pretty good shape when we were done.

CLIMACTIC SCENES DON'T ALWAYS COME TRUE

There's this notion floating around that if you envision something it will happen, but this isn't true. There's nothing magical about the process of envisioning climactic scenes. What I'm talking about when I say envisioning a climactic scene is more about defining a specific direction but in a way that is visual and will stimulate your whole brain.

Envisioning a climactic scene is like pointing to a place on the horizon. From a distance, you might imagine the place you're pointing toward as being wooded with a river near by and a view of a mountain off in the distance. You may squint your eyes and try to pick out the perfect place to build a house.

But when you get there, the place looks completely different. Turns out there's no river but there's a lake and the trees are too high in the mountains to build a house beneath so you settle the land along a meadow.

The reason we envision climactic scenes isn't because they magically become true, it's because they are visual enough to compel our brains.

SHARE AGENCY WITH GOD,
BUT DON'T BECOME CONTROLLING

Stories are no fun if we can completely control them. God has given us limited agency, that's limited power in our stories. It's a blast to control the parts we can control, but we have to learn to love the parts we can't control, too.

When we try to control a climactic scene we become something like bridezilla, yelling at the bridesmaids and cursing the caterers. It shouldn't be this way. Our job is to do our job, that is to point toward a horizon and daily put something on the plot. God will do God's job and all our friends will do theirs. What our stories will be when they are complete is an experiential soup that is partly of our making and partly the making of the people and the God we love. What we get out of the process, then, is full expression of our creativity and yet delightful surprises at every turn.

A CLIMACTIC SCENE CREATES A STORY GAP

Now I should warn you that when you envision a climactic scene you'll create what's called a story gap. A story gap is the space between where a character is and where a character *wants* to be. This is no fun, but paramount to emotional and psychological health.

There are two sides to the *story gap* coin and as you lean into your various stories you'll experience both. The first side of the coin is that a gap will bring a sense of purpose and meaning to your daily experience. This will be a positive experience, helping you know where you are on the existential map. When you envision a climactic scene, you'll have some clarity about where you're going and will experience a slight lifting of the fog.

That said, though, there's a negative feeling associated with a story gap, and it's simply this: *You will realize you aren't where you want to be*. You'll experience this feeling as an internal tension, but don't let it bother you. It's actually a positive thing. Remember, Adam felt the negative side of a story gap the whole time he was naming animals, and yet that tension came back to bless him. Because he was forced to long for Eve, he valued her more and had a more loving relationship with her when she was provided. Tension can always produce a blessing if we have the right attitude.

The tension created with a story gap is humbling but it's ridding us of toxic selfishness. Let's face it, people who get what they want without having to work through tension just become spoiled and hard to be around. Thank God He puts what we want out in the distance so we have to work for it. Otherwise we'd all become divas or dictators.

A CLIMACTIC SCENE CONTRIBUTES TO YOUR DECISION FILTER

While envisioning a climactic scene may cause internal tension, without them, our story filter (read decision filter) would lack clarity. When we envision climactic scenes, we are much less likely to let a lot of unrelated and inappropriate scenes into our lives.

I have a friend in her twenties, for example, who recently quit her job to take a few months off to travel in Brazil. She had another job lined up when she came back to Portland, but knowing she'd likely be settling down when she returned wanted one last hurrah.

She stopped by the house and told me her plan and I sat across from her a little worried. She's like a little sister, honestly, and as I listened I wondered whether or not her plans were slightly reckless. She wasn't sure exactly where she'd stay or who she'd be traveling with and, to be honest, she's a very pretty girl and I'd heard guys in Brazil could come on strong. Perhaps I was being overprotective, but the idea of one last hurrah didn't sit well.

I wasn't her father and so I kept my mouth shut about my concerns. Besides that, she's a good girl, a smart girl who loves God and wants to honor him. At the same time, I remember being in my twenties and loving God and I still made a ton of mistakes. I wondered how to help her understand the importance of having some boundaries as she went off on her last youthful escapade. And then she threw me a soft ball.

You've had lot of adventures, Don. She said. *Any advice for getting the most out of my time in Brazil?*

As a matter of fact I did have some advice. And you'd be proud because I didn't come off as preachy. Instead of listing a bunch of rules, I helped her imagine a climactic scene. I knew a climactic scene had the ability to create a powerful decision filter.

I asked her if she wanted to get married some day, and she said she did. And I asked if she wanted to have kids, and she said she did. And even though all that seemed like it would be a million years away, the truth is she was twenty-five and there was a good chance a husband and kids were around the corner. She agreed this was a possibility and smiled and crossed one of her legs under the other to sit up straighter on the couch.

Okay, I said, *at some point in the next five years or so a scene will likely unfold. You'll be in a hospital somewhere and your husband will be standing next to you and you guys will have just had your first child. There's no guarantee but the odds are with you, right?*

I suppose, she said, smiling a little bigger.

And there you are, I continued, *holding your baby and you'll be in love with your husband and your baby will be beautiful and you'll be doing all the things that young couples do as they start a family. And this scene marks the end of a story, really. It marks the end of your youth and after this scene you'll be entering into another story that is just as exciting but different. This would be the climactic scene of your teens and twenties and after this everything changes.*

All that sounds good, she said. I mean it sounds good five years from now. I want all that. But Don, what does that have to do with my time in Brazil?

Well, here's my advice to you, I said.

While you're in Brazil, don't let any scenes into your story that will interfere with the beauty of the climactic scene you're heading toward when you are married and having your child. You'll have to make some choices. When those choices come up, picture that scene unfolding and if you're about to do anything you'll regret, walk away. Let nothing interfere with the beauty of your future climactic scene.

And within those boundaries, have a blast in Brazil.

I tell this story to illustrate climactic scenes matter. While they may not come true, they contribute to a decision filter that can help us every day.

A CLIMACTIC SCENE WRAPS UP A STORY

Psychologically, we need something to happen to tell us the story is complete. A climactic scene is not unlike the final series of chords in a song. Most songs have a way of wrapping up nicely to give the ear a sense of closure and resolution. These chords cue us to sigh and reflect on what we've heard. Stories are no different. Without a climactic scene, a story can feel unending or unsatisfying.

Sometimes called the obligatory scene, a climactic scene normally involves an event in which all the tension of the story is resolved. When Frodo throws the ring into the fire, for example, Middle Earth is saved. Or when Juliet takes her life to be with Romeo, the story is, well, tragically resolved.

In life, climactic scenes work differently, but they are no less important. When we envision a climactic scene, we deeply penetrate the parts of our brain that activate passion and motivation. Once a scene becomes obligatory, we feel the need to make it happen and so we start working toward that end.

THE ULTIMATE CLIMACTIC SCENE

We encourage you to imagine climactic scenes for each of the stories you are telling. However, there is another climactic scene each of us is looking for that, sadly, may never come. At least not while we are alive.

Movies use climactic scenes to wrap up the tension and give the viewer a sense of resolution. We identify with these scenes, in part, because our souls are looking for resolution too.

When you were growing up in church you probably learned Jesus was the resolution to your problems. I remember hearing a preacher say there was a hole in our souls and we could try to fill that hole with drugs and alcohol and rock and roll music, but the only thing that would fill that void was Jesus. Well, that's a wonderful sentiment and it's certainly a pro-Jesus idea. Unfortunately, though, the idea isn't true. I know plenty of people who know Jesus and yet feel a great sense of longing.

The problem, though, isn't with Jesus, it's with our skewed theology. As has been previously stated, the idea Jesus is a product that will make our troubles go away is something we've borrowed from commercialism. But Jesus isn't a product, He's a living being, and our final healing will come not when we become a Christian, but when we are reunited with Him.

What this means is that even though you have a "relationship with Jesus" you will still experience a longing for Him. But the good news is this longing will be fulfilled. The Apostle Paul talks endlessly in his letters about a hope that will be revealed (1 Peter 1:13) and how Jesus is our *hope in Glory* (Colossians 1:27). For Paul, the climactic scene in the grand human epic hasn't happened yet, but he has hope it will, and he says this hope will not disappoint (Romans 5:5).

The best way to understand where we are, as Christians, in the story of humanity is that we are late in Act II. And Act II is always full of conflict. But this conflict will not last, and while we are in it, we must have patience and courage.

Years ago I rode my bike across America with a small group of friends. I remember one hot afternoon riding through the mountains of New Mexico wondering if the Atlantic Ocean even existed. The landscape seemed so large and the miles so long it felt like the story of riding across a continent would never end.

But it did. It happened suddenly, after weeks and weeks of pedaling. We crested a small hill and saw a lighthouse and each of us cheered and most of us cried as we rode our bikes into the ocean.

It will be like this for those who are betrothed to Christ. There will be a wedding in heaven and when we get there we will sing and dance and feast and drink wine (unless you are Baptist and then you can only have grape juice.)

I bring this up because this is the climactic scene we should use as our ultimate decision filter. When we are wondering what we should do with our lives, when we are making plans with God, let's remember there will come a day when we will kneel before Him and, hopefully, hear him say *well done my good and faithful servant* (Matthew 25).

MODULE EIGHT
Heading Toward Climactic Scenes

Stories are best when they have climactic scenes.

In that single moment when Luke Skywalker destroys The Death Star, he proves himself worthy to be a Jedi, saves the rebellion, and, at least for the time being, defeats his enemy. The reason that scene works is because it's visual proof part of the story is over and the ambition is accomplished.

Life isn't always so clean, but, in lesser shades, we can imagine something like climactic scenes to motivate us toward our ambition and create a finish line that merits a celebration.

The idea here is to give yourself some visual points on the horizon to move toward.

The question to ask when creating a climactic scene is this: *What scene could only take place after my ambition is reached?*

If you want to grow your business, consider planning a ten-thousandth customer party, even if you've only had a few thousand customers so far. And if you could only summit a mountain after you got into shape, write down the summiting of a mountain. Again, the point is to have a visual motivator you can head toward.

In module eight, we want to dream up a climactic scene for each of our ambitions.

Let's Get Started...

1. Reflect on your ambitions, one at a time, and imagine a climactic scene that can only take place once the ambition has been achieved. If you have trouble coming up with climactic scenes, ask your friends for some ideas or use the comment prompt on your Dashboard to stimulate feedback.

2. Transfer each of your climactic scenes to your Storyline Dashboard at **MySubplot.com**

AMBITION 1

A Climactic Scene...

AMBITION 2

A Climactic Scene...

AMBITION 3

A Climactic Scene...

AMBITION 4

A Climactic Scene...

AMBITION 5

A Climactic Scene...

CLOSING THOUGHTS
WHY YOUR STORY MATTERS

STORY SETS THE MORAL COMPASS

The mind learns more through stories than it does through lists and bullet points. Every time we go to the movies we are learning something about life. Make no mistake, screenwriters are teachers when they tell us a story because they are telling us what they believe is worth fighting for.

Every time you hear a story, the moral compass in your mind is adjusted. Good stories help us understand love matters, integrity is important and the world doesn't revolve around us. Other stories may teach us pleasure is king or power is worth killing for. A person's moral compass can be confused as easily as it can be set straight.

I used to think the main way we consumed stories was through movies, books and television. But I don't believe that anymore. The truth is you and I are living stories, whether we like it or not. Each of us wants something and each of us is sacrificing in order to get what we want. If what we want is base, then we are adjusting the moral compass of the people around us, teaching those we love that base things are worth sacrificing for. The main way we consume stories is through each other.

Not long ago I saw an interview with a man named Tom Shadyac. Tom writes movies and has directed many top-grossing films. After an accident in which he suffered tortuous headaches and feared for his life, Tom woke up and realized he'd wasted much of his life pursuing material possessions. When he gained his health back, Tom sold his mansion and his cars and bought a double-wide mobile home where he lives and works today. He says he's happier now than
he's ever been.

Because Tom is living a better story and because countless media sources have picked up on his story, hundreds of thousands of people no longer feel the need to hoard material possessions. Tom's story has shown them a better way to live.

When you begin to live a better story, people will have their moral compasses adjusted and in a real way you'll be saving lives. You'll be teaching people the world is not about us, but about God and His message of love to a broken world. You'll be teaching people the beauty of sacrifice and risk and you'll play a pivotal roll in waking them up from their delusions.

WHAT IF YOUR STORY ISN'T EXCITING?

Often at our conferences we encounter people who don't feel their story has enough significance. They hear stories about people who are building schools in Peru or implementing sex-trafficking legislation and compare themselves.

The truth is, as a writer, I don't live an exciting story either. I mean most of the time you'll find me sitting at a computer typing another book. But this is the story I love and I wouldn't trade it for the world. The work is hard, the risk is huge (try facing Amazon reviews every day) and the objective is clear. I'm honestly not intimidated at all by some of the amazing people I interview because I know both they and I have one thing in common: We've found our story and we are living it with passion.

Once your story is clear and you step into it with abandon, you should feel a sense of contentment. Yes it's true some people live the kinds of stories that make the nightly news, but if you're living your story with God, there's no reason to feel insecure or insignificant. We live in an age where you can become a celebrity by living a great story, but the story of a baker, butcher, plumber or somebody who stays home to raise the kids can be incredibly fulfilling and exciting. The key is to own it, have a great time with it and live your story with passion.

DEALING WITH YOUR NEW LIFE

When you begin to live a great story you should be prepared for people to treat you differently. As your life becomes clear, those who do not have clarity will look to you for wisdom and counsel. This may come as a surprise but don't let it. Be ready. And when I say be ready I mean help people clarify their own ambitions and guide them through the paradigm shift from avoiding to engaging conflict.

You should also be prepared for enemies. When you start living a great story, you will be opposed. There are people who will be threatened by your new life either because they are jealous or because they are used to being the center of attention. Don't be surprised by this. In fact, go ahead and decide what your attitude will be toward those who oppose you. We recommend turning the other cheek, but never apologize for living a great story. In other words, be as kind and accepting as possible but don't stop pushing the plot forward. Live your great story no matter what.

GREAT STORIES MUST END

You'll notice at **MySubplot.com** you can live as many stories as you like. And soon you will be able to archive your stories. We have built this into the system to let you know stories end. All stories end and that's a good thing.

It would be very easy to live a great story, have it end, and go into a depression. After my friends and I rode our bikes across America, almost all of us struggled with depression. Stories can be intense and fulfilling, but they have to end. When they do end, we recommend spending a short season celebrating. And when I say celebrating I mean it. Throw a party, raise your glasses, go on a vacation, get some rest. But don't let this season last too long.

After the celebrating may come an appropriate season of grieving. You can archive your memories and reflect on them but at some point say goodbye to that story and move on. This is where a lot of people get into trouble. They don't move on and so fall back into the existential vacuum.

When I say move on, I mean start planning the next story. In order to stay in Logotherapy we need to have an ambition we're working toward, some conflict to overcome and a climactic scene that is pulling us forward. Treat your stories like swinging ropes in a trapeze. When you let go of one, reach out for the next and continue moving forward.

WHAT TO DO NOW

Now that you've completed the Storyline process, you'll likely see the world differently. And we hope you'll have the framework for living a better story. The trick is to stay disciplined. Not only do we need to follow through with the decisions we've made, but we'll need to keep clutter out. Now that you have a Storyline, you have a decision filter. If you're tempted by some great opportunity that will derail your story, give the decision some serious prayer. At Storyline, we propose you keep things simple and continue moving forward on the stories you've outlined in these pages. Once those stories are done, you can start something new. Finishing is tough business, but it's the business of great storytellers.

PUT A LITTLE SOMETHING ON THE PLOT: Once you've defined your stories, all you have to do is put a little something on the plot. Each day, move the plot toward your climactic scenes. Rather than getting up and doing some random work that doesn't make sense, try to make your work propel your Storyline toward its natural conclusion. This way, you'll only be working on stuff that matters, and the climactic scenes will come sooner than you think.

HELP OTHERS: Now that you've gone through Storyline, you can take others through it and help them live better stories, too. (If you want to become an even better Storyline Guide, attend a conference.) Consider taking somebody else through Storyline. We believe the best way to change the world is to help as many people as possible find their subplot in God's story and we'd be grateful if you lent somebody else a hand creating their Storyline.

JOIN US: A few times a year we host Storyline Conferences. At the conference, we go through the Storyline concepts you read about in this book but also connect with each other and hear from inspiring guests who are living great stories. We'd love to have you at a Storyline Conference. You can learn more at **Storylineblog.com**

THE PSYCHOLOGY BEHIND STORYLINE

STORYLINE IMPROVES MENTAL HEALTH

As a process, Storyline is based on Viktor Frankl's Logotherapy. Frankl is credited with the third Viennese school of psychology. As a psychologist, Viktor Frankl contended with Freud and Adler. Freud posited the primary motivation in man was for pleasure. And Adler was saying the primary motivation in man was power. Frankl believed, however, the primary motivation in man was for a sense of meaning.

What was even more fascinating is Frankl argued a sense of meaning could be gained by having a project to work on and a redemptive perspective toward our suffering. In other words, Frankl argued meaning wasn't a place we arrived at, but rather came through a process we adhered to. Meaning, then, was found in a journey. Frankl called this journey Logotherapy and worked closely with patients to help them find a project they could devote their lives to and also helped them understand how their suffering could be seen through a redemptive lens.

Viktor Frankl's theories were tragically tested in the concentration camps of World War II where he lost his parents and his wife. Despondent in that place, Frankl continued to counsel his fellow prisoners that life expected much of them, even giving them a sense of dignity by convincing them their probable deaths would show the world how evil the Nazi regime was. Because of this, many of the prisoners he counseled survived the atrocities of the Holocaust.

Storyline is based on Logotherapy in the sense it helps people find a redemptive perspective toward their suffering and clarifies ambitions worth living for. When a person creates their Storyline, they enter into Logotherapy and should experience a greater sense of meaning.

Again, Frankl's Logotherapy involves having a project to work on (modules 4 and 8) and a redemptive perspective toward our suffering (modules 3 and 6). Frankl also believed a sense of meaning could be gained by appreciating beauty, including the importance of our roles in loving relationships (module 3).

FURTHER HELP ON REDEEMING YOUR SUFFERING

HELP IN PROCESSING YOUR NEGATIVE TURNS

Some of the negative turns you processed while working through your timeline may have been difficult because they are unresolved. Thinking about these events might have brought up painful emotions. If you'd like some help processing some of the more painful turns in your life, we recommend working through your timeline with a good therapist.

At Storyline, we also recommend a program called OnSite. OnSite is a retreat center located about 45 minutes outside of Nashville and is known for various experiential therapy programs tackling issues like co-dependency, managing our money and relationships.

OnSite has developed a new program called *Prodigal Love* and we recommend this program as a possible next step in living a better story. Here's more information about the program:

ONSITE'S PRODIGAL LOVE PROGRAM

The word "prodigal" means very extravagant or even wastefully generous. The Prodigal Love Program is a place where you can experience the unimaginable love God pours out on us in the midst of our deepest pain, our worst secrets and without pretending. This is not a "religious" program and you don't have to put on a mask here or in front of God to look "good". This program is a relational one where you can come "true faced", drop your guard and let go of your masks, where your deepest wounds can be met with the tenacious love of God and tender mercy of Jesus.

This 4½ day program has, at its foundation, experiential group process supplemented by education and action for change. The process of this program will include identifying and expressing feelings, identifying patterns of self-sabotage, understanding why we have hidden part of ourselves and working through blocks to intimacy in relationships with others and yourself. If you have had a difficult time maintaining a healthy relationship, recognize patterns that are unhealthy or haven't dealt with the hurt from your past, this program is for you. It can help us find healing from our past so we can move into the future that God has for us. If you have coped with life's pain by either trying to "feel good" or to "be good" and neither seems to be working, this program is for you.

The Prodigal Love Program addresses:

Anger or resentment
Relationships
Affirmation
Effects of religious abuse
Living a double life
Feelings
Understanding grace
Difficulty with trust
Making choices and expanding options
Medicators
Family of origin and generational influences
Unlocking creativity and awareness

You can find out more about OnSite at **onsiteworkshops.com** or by calling: **800-341-7432.**

(Onsite has not sponsored this recommendation.)

HOW TO USE MYSUBPLOT.COM

MySubplot is a simple tool, but don't let the simplicity fool you. When you enter a new story into your Dashboard, you'll be locking in your story. Once you write something down, it's fixed and your chances of actually living that story increase.

Here are some tips on getting the most form **MySubplot.com**:

Enter all your current stories: Make sure to follow through and enter your current stories into your Dashboard. This will ensure you fully understand the stories you are trying to live and have complete clarity. The process itself will filter out unnecessary clutter in your life.

Share your stories with friends: As a resource, **MySubplot.com** will grow. The tool is free. We've built a comment section people can use to give you encouragement and tips on following through on the stories you want to live. Once you've entered your stories, share them with friends to create the inciting incident of "going public" with your stories.

Live many stories: Don't limit yourself to only a few stories. Live as many as you like. You might have ten stories going on as a mother, and five more in your career. Plot them all using **MySubplot.com**.

Delete stories that aren't working: Great writers know what to leave out. If you've had a story sitting on your Dashboard for weeks and aren't motivated to move on it, get rid of it and plot out a different story. The idea is to find your passion. Get rid of dead stories and move on to ones that inspire you.

Bookmark Your Story: Either create an icon on your iPhone or bookmark your story on your web browser. MySubplot is not the kind of site that beckons you back each day, but every time you come across it, you'll remember the stories you want to live, and you'll remember your story matters. The changes will come slowly, but they will come. Revisit your story often, and each time study the elements and remind yourself about the stories you are attempting to live.

Your story matters more than a book or a movie or a song. You are the instrument God is using to change the world. We are grateful you're taking your story seriously. Blessings to you as you tell the world a better story.